CW00550177

IMAGES OF THE

SOUTH WALES MINES

To Mick,

With best wishes,

David [illegible]

Other books by David Bellamy

Painting in the Wild

David Bellamy's Watercolour Landscape Course

(both published by HarperCollins)

IMAGES OF THE
SOUTH WALES MINES

DAVID BELLAMY

ALAN SUTTON

First published in the United Kingdom in 1993
Alan Sutton Publishing Limited
Phoenix Mill · Far Thrupp · Stroud · Gloucestershire

First published in the United States of America in 1993
Alan Sutton Publishing Inc · 83 Washington Street · Dover · NH 03820

British Library Cataloguing in Publication Data
Bellamy, David
Images of the South Wales Mines
I. Title

622.334094294
ISBN 0-7509-0412-7

Library of Congress Cataloging in Publication Data applied for

Endpapers: Lewis Merthyr pit-head

Typeset in 13/21 Baskerville
Typesetting and origination by
Alan Sutton Publishing Limited.
Colour separation by Yeo Valley Graphics.
Printed in Great Britain by
Bath Press Colour Books Ltd, Glasgow.

To the memory of my grandfather

JOHN HURN

who was himself a miner before the Great War

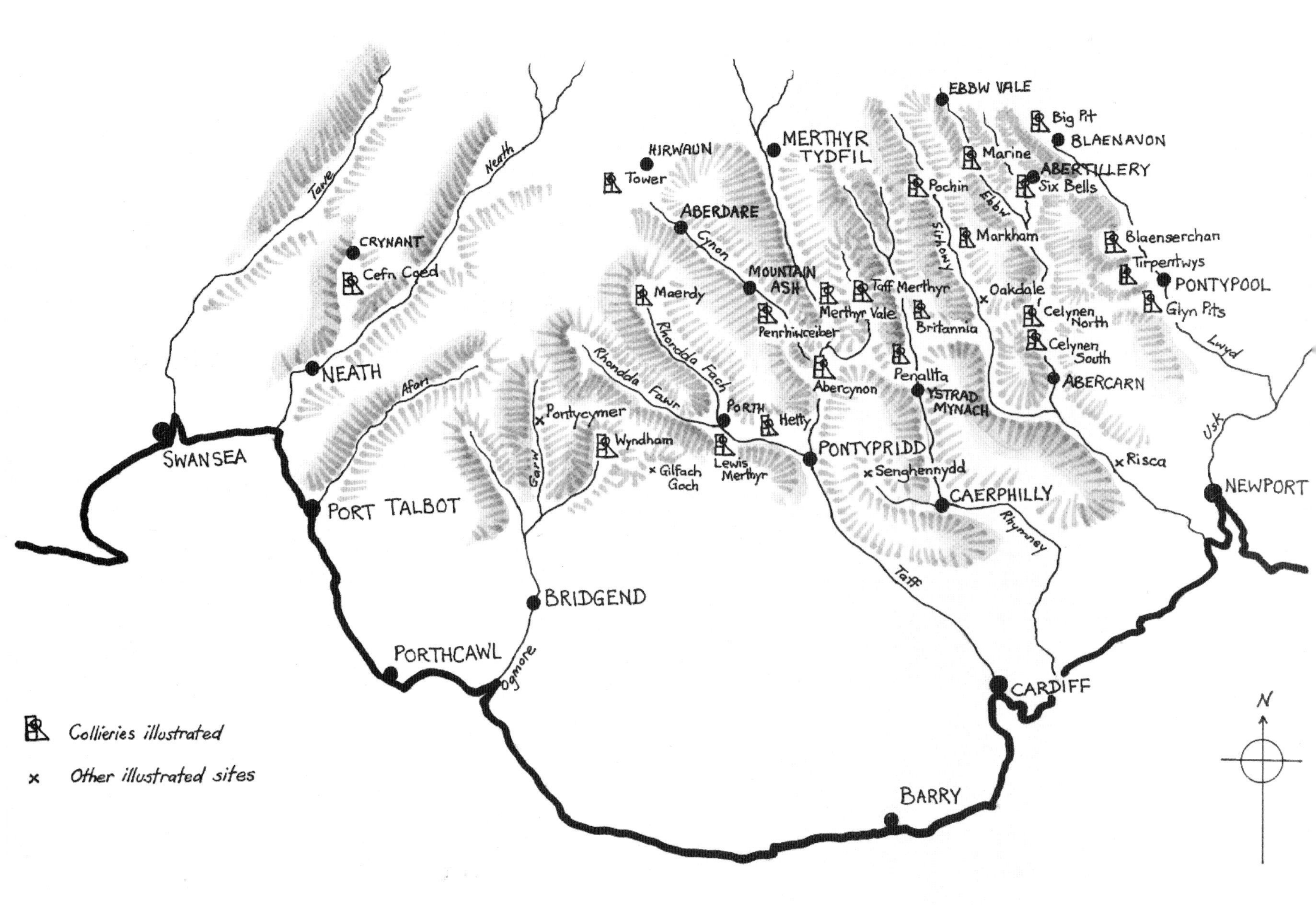

The South Wales Coalfield

Contents

Acknowledgements 8
List of Illustrations 9
Introduction 11

1. The Coming of King Coal 23
2. The Glory Days 37
3. Hardships, Protests and Disasters 59
4. The Rundown of the Coalfield 81
5. Capturing the Scenes 103
6. Following the Trail 125

Glossary of Terms 133
Bibliography 135
Index 136

Acknowledgements

I would like to acknowledge the following people for help given to me in putting this book together: Christine Bellamy; Peter Bennett, Welsh Industrial and Maritime Museum; Gareth Childs, secretary of the Rhondda branch of NALGO; Pat Clarke, Torfaen Museum Trust; Sophie Davies, South Wales Miners' Library; Archibald Eckley; Mrs Annie Gough; Cliff Herbert; Brian Hitchcock, Torfaen Museum Trust; Dr Bill Jones, Welsh Industrial and Maritime Museum; D.P. Todd Jones; James Jones; Lee Jones, training officer, Taff Merthyr Colliery; Hugh Lewis; Robert Merrill, manager, Cefn Coed Colliery Museum; Alan Pritchard, personnel manager, Taff Merthyr Colliery; Jean M. Thomas; Peter Walker, manager, Big Pit Museum; Sarah Wheatley, Rhondda Heritage Park; T.E. Wheatley, director, British Coal Corporation; and most of all Jenny Keal, who supported me throughout the project and made an invaluable contribution to the book, especially on the location visits.

List of Illustrations

Miners off Shift, Maerdy Colliery 13
Roadway, Taff Merthyr 14
Coal Wagons, Tirpentwys Colliery 15
Pit Bank, Markham Colliery 17
Hetty Shaft, Hopkinstown 18
Taff Merthyr Colliery, Bedlinog 21
Wyndham Colliery, Ogmore Vale 24
Abercynon Colliery 25
Glyn Pits, Pontypool 26
Old Coal Dram 28
Cottages at Abertillery 31
Snowfall at Pochin Colliery 32
Pit pony, Pantygasseg Mine 33
Miner Underground 34
Haulage Equipment, Taff Merthyr 36
Dram Loaded with Timber 38
Risca Cottages 39
Steam at Cefn Coed 41
Miner's Safety Lamp 42
Bertie Pit-head, Lewis Merthyr Colliery 44
Coal-face, Big Pit 47
Coal Train Passing Hetty Shaft 48–9
Winter Sunlight, Celynen North Colliery 53
Abercynon Miners' Institute 56
Underground Junction, Big Pit 61
Senghenydd 64
Buckling Girders, Taff Merthyr 66
Marine Colliery, Cwm 69
Pit-head, Tower Colliery 70
Penrhiwceiber Colliery 72
Celynen South Colliery 73
Six Bells Colliery, Abertillery 76–7
Conveyor Belt, Taff Merthyr 78
Merthyr Vale Colliery 80
Pantygasseg Private Mine 82
Tower Colliery from Ffyndaff Opencast Site 83
Stormy Night, Tower Colliery 85
Lewis Merthyr Pit-head 87
Closure of Maerdy Pit, Rhondda Fach 89
Main Roadway, Taff Merthyr 91
Coal-face, Taff Merthyr 92
Starting the Cutter, Taff Merthyr 93

Blaenserchan Colliery 96–7
Site of Oakdale Colliery, Blackwood 100
Penallta Colliery 101
Portrait of Miner, Penallta Colliery 102
Blacksmith's Shop, Big Pit 104
Miners' Cottages, Pontycymer 105
Studio Sketch of Cefn Coed 107
Coming off Shift, Britannia Colliery 108
Detail of Truck, Merthyr Vale 109
Underground Junction, Big Pit 111
Markham Colliery 112–13
Repair Holt (original sketch) 114
Repair Holt (studio sketch) 115
Big Pit, Blaenafon 116
Miner Outside Lamp Room 118
Coming to Bank, Big Pit 120
Paul Tucker, Cutterman 122
Detail of Figures, Britannia Colliery 123
Cefn Coed No. 2 Pit-head 128
Hetty Shaft, Hopkinstown 129
Whistle Inn, Garn yr Erw 131
Tower Colliery, Hirwaun 132

Introduction

In little over 150 years the coal-mining industry in South Wales, which began as simply an adjunct to the metallic industries, grew into an industry of world-wide importance, only to virtually disappear by the late twentieth century. The dramatic change in the valleys landscape, from idyllic rural countryside into a heavily industrialized and polluted area, has almost been equalled by the return to a greener environment. So rapid has been the decline of the industry that in 1993 only one deep mine remains in the coalfield that at its height exactly eighty years ago could boast some 620 pits employing nearly 250,000 workers.

Until fairly recent times, coal-mining had an influence on just about everyone who lived in the valleys of Glamorgan and Gwent, in a manner that no other activity could boast in the whole of Wales. Most English people when thinking of the principality seemed to conjure up images of the coal-mining valleys, to the exclusion of all others. It is not difficult to realize, as a consequence of this overwhelming dependence of valley communities on coal-mining, that an enormous vacuum has been created by the demise of this once-great industry.

My first introduction to the valleys happened in 1962, when I briefly visited Mountain Ash. The strong impression of that day long ago, when as a teenager I saw the long rows of terraced houses, the pit-heads, and witnessed the kindness of the valley people, still lingers. In Pembrokeshire, where I was brought up, the coalfield had virtually ceased working by the time I took my first steps, and although my mother's father had been a miner in the dim past, before he volunteered for the First World War, I knew precious little about coal-mining at that time.

Since leaving school I had always sketched, drawn and painted in some degree, long before I became a full-time artist, and while landscape and figure work appealed greatly there was always something intriguing about industrial scenery. Every so often on a visit to Cardiff I would deliberately route myself past coal-mines to carry out a little sketching, slowly building up a collection. Initially this was done simply for the joy of the experience. It brought a change from the more usual landscapes, and like most artists going through the struggles of their early working years I experimented by painting many kinds of subjects. Objects or scenes tend to be all the more appealing to the artist when they are slightly worn or reveal a hint of decay – not too much, though – and the actual mines were usually full of such visually exciting material. The houses, however, tended to tell a different story. Most of the houses in the valleys exuded a sense of pride, and were well-kept, generally with a flourish of colour around the windows and doors, with painted brick edging contrasting the dressed stone of the walls.

right

Miners off Shift, Maerdy Colliery
In 1875 the sinking of Maerdy Nos 1 and 2 pits was begun by Mordecai Jones of Brecon. By the end of 1876 he had reached the Abergorki Seam. Not long afterwards the shafts were deepened to get at the valuable steam coals lower down. Maerdy Colliery was known as 'Little Moscow' after a remark by a journalist during the 1926 strike.

David Bellamy

In 1985 I bought a miner's cottage on a mountain ridge in Gwent, not all that far from where my mother was born. Here, right on the edge of the South Wales Coalfield, I could not fail to be influenced by the tremendous industrial heritage of the area, and the wealth of painting subjects. Galleries began to request paintings of mines, and although this was just a small part of my work, it did maintain my interest in capturing scenes of pits. With the rundown of the coalfield, this became even more important, but as I was not engaged in an all-out systematic search a number of interesting pits disappeared before I could get round to sketching them. Then in 1988 I began work on an exhibition to highlight threats to the Welsh landscape by inappropriate and insensitive development, in conjunction with the Campaign for the Protection of Rural Wales. This led to a more planned campaign for sketching material in the valleys, and although it did not involve coal-mines directly I was seeking out good examples of reclamation to highlight as positive aspects for the exhibition. At one point I sat in the car sketching the awesome phurnacite works at Abercwmboi. Belching out smoke, flames and fumes it resembled Victorian images of industrial hell. Orange, black and grey smoke curled round the blackened girders and chimneys, accompanied by a pungent smell that gave one the impulse to get away as fast as

Roadway, Taff Merthyr

← Girder for Becorit haulage system

← Conveyor belt for coal

Coal Wagons, Tirpentwys Colliery

In May 1931 a violent storm rent the valley, sending torrents down the slopes. Many pit horses were drowned, and furniture, pigs and chickens, among other things, were swept down the valley by the raging floods. The spoil slopes on which the railway sidings stood were torn away. Railway wagons were tossed down the slope like toys, in a scene of utter devastation, as though an earthquake had hit the area.

The colliery winding gear at Tirpentwys – 'the land on top of the earth' – was unusual in having the two winding wheels one above the other. In 1902 the winding cable broke and eight miners perished when the cage plummeted to the pit bottom. Archibald Eckley reckoned there were 700 to 800 men and 112 horses at the pit in its prime. The colliery was closed in 1969, but its seams continued to be worked via the Hafodyrynys pit for some time after.

possible. Although I sketched it in charcoal to illustrate how awful the place appeared, it did excite me enormously from an artistic viewpoint. But without doubt it was a scene that belonged to the eighteenth century.

About this time I was invited to give a demonstration of watercolour painting to the Ystradyfodwg Art Society. The chapel hall in Treorchy was crammed to the rafters that night, with art societies from all over the Rhondda and further afield. It was a welcome that I'll never forget. Afterwards the minister came up to me and said 'I wish I could pack them in like that on a Sunday'. It was good to see that the arts were still alive and flourishing in the Rhondda.

When Maerdy Colliery, the last working pit in the Rhondda, closed down just before Christmas 1990, I witnessed the last rites on the history of coal-mining in the valley. Being there on that miserable wet December day had a profound effect on me, so profound that it became the turning point that instilled in me a desire to record these events, as the story of coal-mining in South Wales dramatically drew to a close. From then on I took a closer look at what was happening in the coalfield. Also by then I had accumulated quite a considerable amount of visual material on coal-mining.

In late 1991 David Williams, of the New Gallery in Mumbles, asked if I would put on an exhibition of mining paintings, to which I agreed. Looking through the material I had available it dawned on me that it would be a dreadful waste to produce all the paintings and not publish them in book form. This feeling was strengthened when I realized how rapidly the coalfield was being phased out. Soon it would all be gone. I began to talk to people and visit the mining museums where I found a wealth of material. It soon became clear to me that here was something that had to be published.

From then on I worked feverishly on the project, often visiting sites where I knew there was little to see, mainly in order to soak up the atmosphere. Usually something came of each visit. The valleys folk love to talk about their community, and at times my methods of engaging them in conversation bordered on the ridiculous. One ex-miner at Pontycymer in the Garw Valley became rather concerned when I stood precariously on the

Pit Bank, Markham Colliery

With strong lines formed by the girders criss-crossing in the background and above the cage, it was necessary to subdue most of these, and eliminate a few, otherwise the men with the dram would easily be overwhelmed by detail.

parapet of the railway bridge, trying to improve my angle of vision while sketching. The subsequent conversation proved to be very interesting. However, it is not really necessary to go to quite such lengths in order to meet an ex-miner in the South Wales valleys!

This book is by no means a definitive work on the history of coal-mining in South Wales; rather it aims to give a flavour of what life was like in the coalfield, both the visual aspect and from the personal side, with anecdotes collected from the people themselves. This is backed with a brief outline of the major events in almost two centuries of mining history. It is a celebration of the proud history of the valley communities. While there has been much sadness and tragedy, what has mainly impressed me has been the spirit of the people, and the colour and the humour of the miners, which has shone through even at the blackest of times. It is easy to accentuate the romantic view of the collier, as portrayed in novel and film, a view so far from the truth. Most of the time digging out the coal has been a hard, dangerous and filthy task often accompanied by pain and suffering.

When, in this already harsh existence the mining communities have had to suffer deprivation, indignity and merciless, savage iniquities inflicted upon them by indifferent employers and those in power, their morale and human vitality have remained unshaken. This was just as true in the 1980s as it was in the 1840s. Working on the book has at times brought feelings of sadness, anger and disgust, as well as admiration and amazement, the more I learned of how the mining communities have been treated.

Central to the image of the pit village stood the lattice-work metal structures of the pit-head winding gear, grown out of necessity and practicality, rather than conforming to any aesthetic purpose. These tall structures surrounded by a conglomeration of various architectural shapes in some ways resembled the superstructure of a battleship, and although complex to draw, provided quite a challenge to me. The more I sketched, the more excited I became. Some only see them as ugly, hideous eyesores from a byegone age, their sight perhaps blighted by the memory of hardship and bitter struggle. However, the eye trained in critical observation can gain a great degree of satisfaction and

Hetty Shaft, Hopkinstown

Rain was lashing directly into my face as I sketched the winding gear from high up on the foot-bridge across the railway line. Being accurate on such occasions is not easy.

aesthetic pleasure from the way sunlight falls on an intricate section of girders, for example, or glints on the winding sheaves as they spin rapidly round.

While my immediate visual response created a desire to record the scene on paper, the manner in which I worked was strongly influenced by my emotional feelings towards the subject. Knowing something about the history of a pit – perhaps a disaster – brought forth a deeper inner drive to create a more powerful painting. This is really painting from the heart. Working on the mines in different weather and lighting conditions provided endless variations in subject treatment, so necessary when working on a whole book or exhibition. I had already sketched Tower Colliery at Hirwaun, for example, when I felt the need for a truly wild setting, with the pit-head in a central position. So I returned to Tower Colliery on a gloriously wild winter evening when rain lashed across the yard, caught in the orange glow of the lights.

Inextricably bound up with the coalfield were the railways, and I felt it was important to portray the age of steam in some scenes. This involved quite a bit of research. Railways lend themselves to atmospheric pictures, and to me it is vital to put across a strong sense of mood, whatever type of subject is being painted.

Another indispensable ingredient is achieving the feeling of the character of a place: the houses must look like the houses of the South Wales valleys, not just any old architectural style. It was important to me to produce an overall picture of the valley communities, rather than just the coal-mines themselves. One of the hardest features to find was an aesthetically pleasing slag-heap!

Looking through old photographs of the mines around the turn of the century made me envious of the quality of the subject material available to artists in those days. Gray's Mine in Abertillery in particular looked fascinating, compositionally, with the pit working at several different levels. With their tall chimneys and wreathed in clouds of smoke and steam, these earlier mines exuded considerable atmosphere, rarely seen in the industries of today. This, of course, is a good thing, as atmospheric and visual pollution on such a scale made the immediate environs of the mines miserable to inhabit.

The first four chapters outline the background history, mainly in chronological order, moving from the early pioneering days in chapter one, through to the heyday of the coalfield or the 'blood and cloth cap era' as Peter Walker of Big Pit put it. In chapter three we look at some of the disasters and hardships experienced over the years, while chapter four discusses the gradual demise of the coalfield. Chapter five illustrates how the scenes were captured on paper, including some of the techniques involved. The reconstructed paintings in particular require an explanation of methods adopted, as in most cases these needed a fair degree of detective work. Both artist and non-artist should find this aspect of interest. In Wales we have a rich seam of artists of all abilities, and I hope this book will inspire many to dig out their old sketches and photographs, and have a go at bringing a bit more of history to life. I am certain that there is a large store of untapped

Taff Merthyr Colliery, Bedlinog

Taff Merthyr was sunk between 1924 and 1926 by the Powell Duffryn Group, starting to produce coal directly after the General Strike. It had a deepest working level of 2,093 feet. Up to nine tonnes of coal can be brought up in the cage on each wind. During its peak years in the 1930s it employed over 1,600 men and output stood at an annual average of 600,000 tonnes. It closed in 1993.

pictorial material out there. Finally, chapter six gives details of where to find existing sites of interest to those keen on coal-mining history. A glossary is included at the end in order to explain some of the more obscure words mentioned in the text that might not be generally understood by those not involved in the coal industry.

My selection of scenes to include in the book has of course been very personal, but naturally dictated by the availability of visual reference material. Because of the severe lack of subject material during the main period of working on this project, it has been impossible to cover the entire coalfield. That would have been impracticable in a book of this size, anyway. Nevertheless, I have tried to include as many of the valley communities as possible, given the restrictions. With regard to the text, so much is available that I have had the opposite problem!

At one time the coalfield stretched from Pembrokeshire in the west to Pontypool in the east, and yet as I write deep mining in South Wales is almost at a close. Sadly, once pits close they can never be reopened. I have not included the Pembrokeshire part of the coalfield in this work, as I want to keep the content within the boundaries of the South Wales valleys, with their own very distinctive and unique character. In putting together this book many people have helped me, and I would like to thank all those people who have contributed in some way. Working on the project and meeting so many interesting characters has given me enormous pleasure, but a pleasure tinged with a sadness that most of the scenes in this book and a way of life no longer exist.

CHAPTER ONE

The Coming of King Coal

Wyndham Colliery, Ogmore Vale

Sinking of the shafts at Wyndham Colliery was begun in 1865 by Brogden and Sons of Tondu. It was later taken over by Norths' Navigation Collieries and then Cory Brothers in 1906. Here the pit is seen as it looked around the turn of the century, and is one I definitely did not sketch! During my research I came across an old photograph illustrating the colliery with its warped boarding and pulley wheels for operating the screens. As there was no other way of depicting this type of scene I have broken my personal rulebook and copied part of the photograph, with the kind permission of the Welsh Industrial and Maritime Museum. The colliery site is now a playing field, with little evidence of its former use.

Although coal was used to a small degree by the Romans occupying Britain, the abundance of timber made it rather superfluous over the following centuries. During the sixteenth century a heavy demand for timber began, and thus coal became a viable alternative. It was first mined in quantity in the north east of England and grew in popularity during the next two centuries.

At the beginning of the nineteenth century the valleys of South Wales lay unspoilt and tranquil, their rivers clean and sparkling, with a very sparse rural population. Until then mining for coal had been restricted to the edges of the coalfield where coal could be found near the surface, and hence was easier to extract. From the end of the sixteenth century the copper industry was developed, following the discovery, by Abraham Darby of Coalbrookdale, that metals could be smelted by using coal. A great amount of coal was necessary in the smelting process: four and a half tons were needed to reduce one ton of copper ore to the final product. Consequently it was far cheaper to bring copper ore to South Wales from Cornwall and North Wales than to transport huge quantities of coal.

At Neath and Swansea the coalfield lies close to the sea, making these excellent locations to bring in the ore by ship. Moving coal over land in large quantities was extremely difficult. With seams outcropping along the valley sides, the coal could be reached without deep mining, which was impossible at the time. The Neath area quickly became Britain's premier copper-smelting centre. Expansion was rapid, and Swansea, with its better port

Abercynon Colliery

The colliery was sunk in 1896 and in March 1975 was linked underground to the Lady Windsor Colliery at Ynysybwl in a neighbouring valley.

facilities soon overtook Neath. By the mid-nineteenth century Swansea produced over half the world's copper. A large concentration of copper works grew up along the banks of the River Tawe in the lower Swansea valley.

Meanwhile, on the north-eastern side of the coalfield the iron industry grew, with Merthyr Tydfil as the main production centre. There, the abundance of iron ore, limestone, and many streams to provide water, made it an ideal location for the iron industry once coal replaced timber in the smelting process. From this grew an insatiable demand for coal to fire the furnaces. Merthyr Tydfil, then the largest town in Wales, became the 'iron capital of the

Glyn Pits, Pontypool

This sketch shows the engine house with part of the old Cornish type of beam engine. The colliery was begun in the 1840s by Capel Hanbury Leigh, and the engine remained in use until production ceased in 1932.

world'. By 1840 coal was also being sold to other industries and for use in heating the home. In addition, much of it was exported, mainly to France. At this time the main means of transport inland was along the canals, a very slow process.

Until the nineteenth century the only method used for reaching the coal was by outcropping – digging up coal found near the surface once the topsoil had been removed, a process similar to the opencast mining of today. Bell pits were a further development. These comprised a vertical shaft below which a chamber was opened out once the coal seam was reached, not far below the surface. The coal was hauled up the shaft in buckets pulled by a winch. Usually when the roof collapsed the pit was abandoned. As one can imagine, this system could not have been terribly popular with the miners! Drift mines were also introduced. These burrowed into hillsides, either level or at a slant, and of course are still in use today in the many private mines.

In the early nineteenth century coal-mining expanded rapidly and with it the capability of opening up deep mines. These began to be opened in the Cynon Valley by such pioneers as John Nixon and Thomas Powell. Nixon had seen coal fired in Thames' steamboats without producing any smoke, and this prompted him to visit Wales to see for himself this amazing steam coal. Not long afterwards the rich coal measures of the Rhondda were reached with deep mining. Native Welshmen such as George Insole, Walter Coffin and David Davies of Llandinam were among the

Old Coal Dram

This scene was reconstructed by taking a delightfully rusty old dram from Cefn Coed Colliery Museum, adding the chains and wheel from Big Pit, plus two miners from Taff Merthyr, and placing it a background shed based on yet another location. The miners have been clothed in turn-of-the-century garb and a strong sense of sunlight was added to pick out the dram clearly.

pioneer mine owners. David Davies in particular became the most prominent coal-mine owner in the Rhondda. It was he who was instrumental in developing Barry Docks in 1884, as Cardiff Docks were becoming congested, and this led to great competition between the two ports. By 1887 Davies had set up the huge Ocean Coal Company.

Soon, as the railways began to make inroads into the valleys, canals became redundant. The Taff Vale Railway was built up to the head of the Rhondda Fawr. Rapidly the Rhondda overtook every other valley in the production of coal, to become the most famous coal-producing area in the world. Other valleys rapidly followed suit, including those in Monmouthshire. In West Glamorgan and Carmarthenshire the anthracite coalfield did not expand as spectacularly as the steam coalfield because of the problems using anthracite in steam-engines and in the home.

Sinking a coal-mine involved taking a considerable financial gamble for these early mine developers. Some of the coal seams were exceptionally deep and prone to geological problems. Sinking a shaft so far underground proved to be a costly business and could involve up to two years' work before the first dram of coal arrived at the surface. Understandably some mines were abandoned before any coal was actually brought to the surface. At one of Davies' sites digging had gone on for some fifteen months without any sign of coal, when suddenly the miners struck a rich seam – just as Davies had given up any hope. In addition to the initial outlay, the owners had to pay a royalty to the landowner on every dram of coal.

To sink these deep pits, teams of sinkers (clad in their distinctive garb of long coats and large hats with wide brims overhanging the backs of their necks to protect them from falling stones and water) carried out the task of digging out the shaft. They descended the shaft in a large bucket, or 'kibble', winched down on the end of a chain. Sinking the shaft was a back-breaking, wet job, with inevitable danger, and so difficult that sinkers worked less hours than colliers. The sinkers would set up their shanty one-storey accommodation near the pit, and though these huts were meant only to be temporary, some have remained in existence to the present day.

When the shaft sinking was complete most of the sinkers would move on to the next site. James Jones of Maerdy well remembers his grandfather of the same name, who sank numbers 1 and 2 pits at Maerdy. 'Grandfather was an intimidating man of 6 feet 2 inches height with a long white beard. There were four sinkers' huts and my mother was born in one. When there were fights in the Maerdy Hotel the police wouldn't intervene – they would call on Grandfather who would go in and bang a few heads together! He was an extremely strict man who would not allow his children to go to bed until he had arrived home, even if it was 2 a.m!

'On 23rd December 1885 an explosion occurred in the pit and grandfather went down the mine to help. The first person he came across was his son-in-law, standing up against a dram, dead. Nearby another relative stood dead where he had been at work. In all he brought 25 miners out that night.' With eighty-one miners killed in the catastrophe it was a tragic Christmas for the Maerdy community that year.

Explosions were caused by firedamp – methane gas mixed with air in sufficient proportions to cause ignition when exposed to a flame. Sir Humphrey Davy invented a safety lamp as early as 1815, but this gave out less light than a candle, so initially there was a lot of resistance by the miners, as it slowed down their work.

Until then the sole means of illumination was the candle – a highly dangerous practice in a gassy mine. At that time the method of getting rid of gas proved especially hazardous, if not outright suicidal. This was carried out by 'firemen', who either covered themselves with wet sacking or dampened their coats, to afford at least a little protection. With a candle fastened to the end of a long pole, the fireman would lay down on the floor like some monk taking a severe penitence. While on the floor the candle was lit, and as gas tended to stay closer to the roof, the fireman would cover his head and raise the candle away from himself to light the gas.

Cottages at Abertillery

The growth of the iron and coal industries in South Wales created vast employment, and so brought with it rapid immigration to Glamorgan and Monmouthshire. Wages in the coal industry were far better than those in agriculture. Many quarrymen from North Wales moved south, believing that a better future awaited them in the coal-mines. People not only flooded in from the other Welsh counties, but from the late nineteenth century onwards they came from Somerset, Gloucestershire, Herefordshire and many other English counties. Large numbers came in search of work from Ireland, as well as many from Scotland. Some even came from as far afield as Spain and Italy. Quickly the population of the Rhondda doubled, then trebled, becoming very cosmopolitan.

At the beginning of the industry even children barely six years old worked underground. The very young, including girls, were

Snowfall at Pochin Colliery

The pit stood high above the Sirhowy river, and sinking began in 1876. Geological problems suspended work for some time, until the beginning of the 1880s. Because of the overpowering geometrical design of parallel horizontal lines near the foreground, a snowstorm has been added to subdue the effect. Railway wagons sketched at the Welsh Industrial and Maritime Museum have been included with the livery of the Tredegar Iron and Coal Company. The pit was named after one of the company directors.

Pit Pony, Pantygasseg Mine
This is a lovely old private mine not far from the Tirpentwys site. I was kindly given permission to sketch, though to reach the best subjects I first of all had to negotiate a veritable sea of mud. Sunlight shafted beautifully through gaps in the wall as I sketched. The mine is a drift, actually going upwards, so the horse had to haul an empty dram up a shallow incline to the face, and then slow the dram down on its way out with a full load.

mainly employed as door-keepers, opening and closing doors in the underground roadways in order to control ventilation. This involved many hours standing alone in the dark with a primitive light for about twopence a day. Often they would fall asleep, which could mean that they would get a beating. For some, however, it would end in tragedy, with a dram running over their legs. Accidents were all too common. As the mining regulations were in English the risks were particularly great for the Welsh speakers. Older children dragged carts of coal from the coal-face, harnessed like animals. Children under ten were forbidden to work underground once an Act of Parliament was passed in 1842, though even after this many owners turned a blind eye and continued this iniquity. Women also worked underground until 1842, hauling coal wagons half-naked, the chains chafing their bodies. In the very early days, sledges or boxes had to be dragged through tunnels too low for ponies to be used. This demanded a toughness equal to that of the men. All were expected to work twelve-hour shifts each day, six days a week. This pattern was only broken when they were thrown out of work by a slump in the demand for coal. It was an extremely hard and cruel existence, working in a world of darkness.

Miner Underground

Extracting coal in the nineteenth century was done by sheer hard labour. The collier would use a mandril for hewing out the coal, sometimes kneeling in murky water or lying on his side in an awkward position. Both hewing and shovelling out the coal in these cramped conditions exerted a dreadful strain on the men, their bodies often twisted in unnatural positions for most of the shift. After a short while they would be soaking from perspiration, and would have to stay like that until the end of the shift. The colliers drank water or cold tea and usually carried sandwiches in a metal 'tommy box'. This would normally keep out the dust and mice. Mice and rats in some ways were regarded as friends, for if they behaved strangely it was usually a sure sign that the roof was about to collapse, or something equally dreadful was about to happen. Ponies too, seemed to have an acute sense of danger.

In places the coal seam would be loosened first with gunpowder. Firstly holes would be drilled above the seam using a tool that looked like a super-long brace and bit – a process known as 'top-holing'. Next, the gunpowder would be inserted, and this was plugged with clay. The shotfirer would then light a fuse, usually a straw filled with gunpowder, and retire at speed to a safe distance. Hopefully the blast would loosen the coal. Over-liberal use of gunpowder would at times not only bring down the coal but the roof as well, and on occasion the explosion could ignite gas and cause an even greater explosion.

The 'pillar and stall' technique primarily used at this time remained the mainstay method of coal-mining in South Wales until the late nineteenth century, although some mines continued with the technique beyond this. A series of stalls, several yards wide were strung out along the coal-face, with pillars of coal and rock left between the stalls to support the roof. Normally each of the stalls was the responsibility of a collier and a boy, who was often a relative. It was a slow and dangerous manner of working the coal, in appalling conditions. As Orwell says in *The Road to Wigan Pier*, 'Most of the things one imagines in hell are there – heat, noise, confusion, darkness, foul air, and, above all, unbearably cramped space'.

Horses were increasingly used for haulage along the main roadways from 1840 onwards, and would be kept stabled underground permanently, rarely seeing the light of day. They were also employed on winding up fairly shallow mines, using a 'horse-gin', but here the horses were eventually replaced by a water-balance method whereby an empty dram would be placed on a water-bucket at the top of the shaft, and then the bucket filled with water. The weight of the full bucket sent it to the bottom of the shaft, at the same time pulling up a coal-laden dram on an empty bucket from below. It was not until the 1870s that these methods were overtaken by the tall pit-head winding gear with metal cages being pulled up and down the shafts on steel ropes by steam engines. Guide rails ran down the shaft to keep the cages steady as they moved up and down. The introduction of cages enabled the coal drams filled at the coal-face to be brought to the surface – a tremendous improvement in the moving of coal. Initially wood was used in the construction of the pit-head structures, but this was gradually replaced by the metal lattice-work structures so symbolic of the coal-mines of South Wales.

Haulage Equipment, Taff Merthyr

The valleys of South Wales were changing dramatically. Pit villages were springing up, soon to be blackened by the grime of heavy industry. Jean Thomas in her poem 'Pit Town' conjures up marvellous imagery:

> . . . burrowings of human moles who carve
> satanic landscapes, charcoal pyramids
> that smoulder threats, unstable rumblings,
> as long-dead forests, petrified, rise up
>
> to haunt the ruined valley, blemish sky
> with hollow, gloomy graveworks – robbed, defiled
> vibrating faint metallic requiems:
> the chant of steel on subterranean walls.

CHAPTER TWO

The Glory Days

By the end of the nineteenth century South Wales, after a slow start, had become one of the most important coal-producing areas in the world. The coalfield at that time employed as much as ten per cent of the Welsh population. Coal had become indispensable to the whole of British industry, powering railways, ships and factory machinery, smelting metals, as well as warming homes. The gradual opening up of the railways into each of the valleys in the middle of the century was the crucial link in the export trade and dictated the development of new mines. Trains left with coal and brought in wood for pit props. The great docks of Cardiff, Newport, Barry and Penarth in the south east, and Swansea, Llanelli and Port Talbot in the west, flourished and grew dramatically. In 1852 the Taff Vale Railway was linked to the Great Western Railway, opening up new possibilities. Cardiff grew from being a small village at the start of the century into the world's premier coal exporting port a hundred years later.

Dram Loaded with Timber

The coal companies achieved varying successes. Some mines produced little good-quality coal, and the costs of sinking them crippled quite a number of entrepreneurs. Many of the smaller companies were taken over by the more powerful ones, and by the turn of the century the giant 'combines', such as the Cambrian, were coming into being. At this time also steam coal was experiencing a boom period which enabled the combines to grow fatter on increasing profits.

When the Royal Navy approved the use of Welsh steam coal it soon became popular with other navies, and was used in shipping generally. Welsh coal gave more power for less smoke, which afforded a tremendous advantage in a naval engagement. It was sent out to coaling stations all over the world, thus literally fuelling the British Empire. Expansion of the railways further contributed significantly to the use of steam coal. Coal had now become the backbone of the nation's power.

Parallel with the growth of the mines came the pit villages. Rows of grimy terraced houses, blackened by coal-dust, began to appear along the valley sides. These were mainly built in a haphazard manner with little consideration given to planning. Overcrowding was rife, with immigration outstripping the availability of houses. Some coal-owners insisted that their employees took in lodgers, which added to the problems of the many large families. Thirteen people in a two-up two-down was

The roofs glistened in the soft drizzle. On the left the houses are brick-coloured, on the right a dark drab colour, all with their characteristic valleys feature of highlighted windows in white. Below the river Ebbw ran its artificial course beside the noisy highway.

Risca Cottages

not uncommon, and there were even instances of up to twenty-one persons living under the same roof! In some cases a curtain drawn across the room would separate families. To a degree the shift system worked well here, for as one miner vacated his bed to go to work, another would come off shift and use the same bed. Even bathing seemed to be a very sociable occasion, with perhaps five or six miners bathing in the tin bath on a rota system – using the same water. No one seemed to mind if bath-time coincided with a visit from the women next door!

The prospect of an arduous, back-breaking job in a dangerous, dark and grimy environment did not seem to discourage most young lads from wanting to start work down the pit at the earliest opportunity. However, it would be wrong to class all miners as reckless heroes desperate to get down the pit the moment they were out of nappies. Many young lads were not too eager to start work and some were naturally scared at the prospect of the darkness, danger and foul atmosphere that lurked in the mines on every shift. But for most males in the valleys going down the pit was the only work available.

Todd Jones of Crynant began working at Cefn Coed around 1935–6. 'It was hard in them days, mind. We cut coal by hand using a mandril. It was difficult to push the shovel into uneven coal.' He earned about 17 shillings and ninepence per week in those days, when beer was sixpence a pint. Miners had to pay for their own tools and these included not just the mandril and shovel, but a hatchet for cutting the notches in roof supports,

Steam at Cefn Coed

Clouds of steam accentuate the outline of the dark locomotive as it pulls away from the screens. I originally sketched the locomotive at the Dean Forest Railway Centre.

prising bars, coal boxes as well as other minor items. Added to this were replacement handles and glass for the lamps. Entering the cage and going down the shaft at thirty feet per second was a sobering moment which made many nervous, no matter how many times they had gone down before. The blackness was absolute and at the turn of the century the miners' lights could barely reach beyond a few inches. In the confined space noises were magnified, and sudden, sharp sounds would set nerves jumping. In 1815 Sir Humphrey Davy invented the safety lamp, but this actually only gave out one-eighth the light strength of a candle. If methane gas entered a 'Davy' lamp and ignited, the flame would not escape through the gauze. These lamps often went out, however, and had to be relit from underground lamp stations. This involved the miner and his butty having to leave work and go to relight the lamp, thus depriving them of work-time. Archibald Eckley, who worked for over fifty years at Tirpentwys Colliery near Pontypool, remembers the problem well: 'The old oil lamp – if he went out he was locked, and you couldn't open him. So you had to go to the man with a lighter, half a mile away from the coal-face on the main road where there was plenty of air and it was safer.' The lamps were generally hung from the belt, making it rather awkward when walking along.

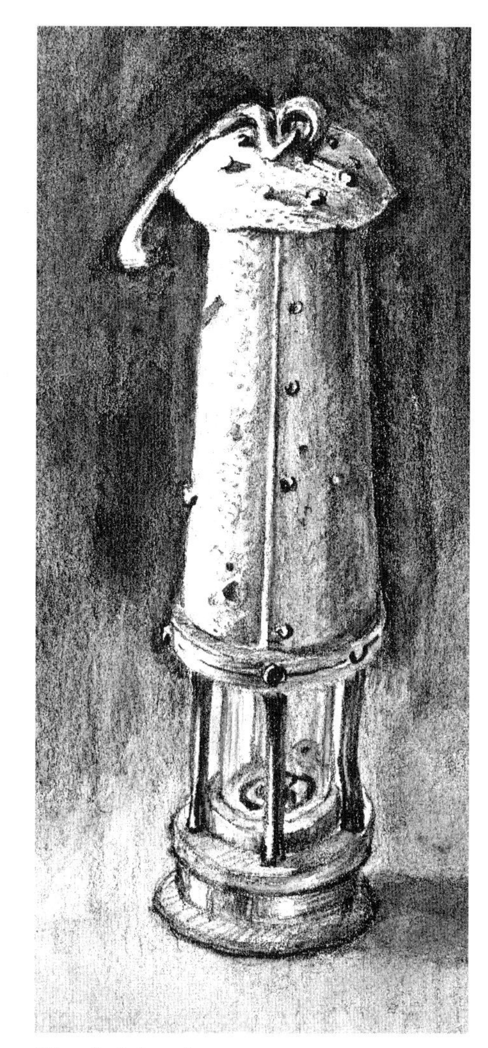

Miner's Safety Lamp

Safety lamps were used to detect gas underground. The presence of methane gas was evident by the shape and colour of the flame in the lamp, but this system was complicated because the level of gas varied considerably even within a small area. It tended to hang around cracks and corners, places where it was awkward to employ the lamp. Some mines were more prone than others to gas problems, as gas pockets were more likely to occur in the softer coal seams. If gas was detected the pit would be evacuated and the ventilation system would be directed through the problem area.

The dangers of firedamp were ever present underground. Even a stone dropping for some distance down the shaft could ignite gas drawn in its wake on striking an object, and so cause an explosion. A mandril striking stone could also cause ignition. In some cases dust explosions rent the mine by fire shooting along the roadways and tunnels, being fed on thick airborne coal-dust. The roadways and workings were deliberately designed to provide a constant flow of air throughout, as good ventilation inhibited the build-up of gas. Most mines had two shafts each with its own separate pit-head winding gear, though some had a level entering the valley side lower down. One of the shafts became the 'upcast shaft' where the air was drawn upwards by the ventilation system, and the other became the 'downcast shaft' where the fresh air was sucked into the pit. In the early days this was achieved by installing a furnace at the bottom of the upcast shaft: the hot air rose, sucking out the stale air from the underground spaces, while fresh air was sucked into the downcast shaft. This system was not without its problems, though, as the furnace itself would at times ignite firedamp. Later large fans sited at the top of the upcast shaft were used to draw out the stale air.

During the second half of the nineteenth century mechanized methods of underground haulage began to be introduced. Horses were expensive to feed and look after, so engines powered by compressed air gradually replaced them. A line of drams would be hauled along the roadways to pit bottom by the engines, using long wire cables. Compressed air became available in the 1870s and was used to power many tools and machines in the coal-mine. Horses were still in use in the deep mines until well into the

mid-twentieth century, though. Todd Jones remembers one animal in particular, for its cunning. On one heading the haulier would walk alongside the wagon to 'sprag' the wheels – that is, to stop progress by pushing a pole through the spokes. At a narrow part of the heading the horse knew that on the way down with a full dram the haulier could not walk beside it. At this point the horse would stop, and aware that nothing could be done, it would stay put. It only restarted when it saw the light of the haulier appearing in front, having walked a considerable way round to get to the front of the animal!

In the 1870s many South Wales pits abandoned the old 'pillar and stall' method of face-working, and introduced the 'longwall' system. With this method the whole coal-face was worked at the same time. Colliers advanced the coal-face as they mined, filling their own dram immediately behind, or using a curling box to transport coal to the dram. Wooden pit props replaced the pillars, and each miner was responsible for his own props. Later, the advent of conveyor belts speeded things up, with one belt behind the face taking away the coal and dropping it on to another belt running down the roadway towards pit bottom.

Coal was carried in the drams to the surface, where it was tipped through screens, which were usually steel bars set a few inches apart. These allowed the small coal to fall through and thus be separated from the large coal. Further along the process the waste – stone, fireclay or pyrites – was removed by hand. After this the coal went through a crusher followed by the washery

left

Bertie Pit-head, Lewis Merthyr Colliery
The two shafts on the Lewis Merthyr site were named after the owner's sons, Trevor and Bertie. This view is seen from the end of Bryn Eirw Street, which forms an excellent lead-in to the focal point. To give the scene a sense of earlier times I have omitted cars, television aerials and the like, and dressed the miners coming off shift in clothes of less modern times. The addition of clouds of steam emphasizes the feeling of earlier times.

which eliminated the muck attached to the coal. Each collier marked his own dram with chalk to identify his workload, which was weighed on the surface. From around 1860 miners were allowed to appoint a check-weighman to check that they were not being short-changed by the company.

To compound the hardness of working underground, the attitude of many coal-owners was particularly harsh. Some owners looked upon the loss of a horse or a dram as being more disastrous than the death of a miner; they could usually get away without paying compensation to the widow, but the loss of a horse meant they had to buy a new one. Owners would blame the cause of explosions on the miners smoking underground. They rarely kept any medical facilities at the mines and generally skimped on anything to do with safety. Jean Thomas puts it succinctly in her poem 'Coal-Owners':

> Unmoved, the dukes of darkness reign,
> Immune to poverty and pain:
> Keeping profit margins high,
> Tonnage rising, miners die.

Towards the end of the century the coal-owners had their own association, but bitterly opposed any union for the miners. Any miner found joining a trade union was automatically sacked. In order to avoid detection, union membership tabs were often sewn inside the lining of miners' coats. A number of attempts were made to set up unions, but in the early days these were often defeated by the owners' hostility and the importation of 'blackleg' labour from outside the area. In 1898, however, the need for strong unity had become apparent and The South Wales Miners Federation was formed. By involving itself more in the domestic and social life of the mining communities than was normal for a trade union, 'the Fed' grew in strength to become the largest single union in Great Britain by 1914. A campaign was set up to encourage miners to join the union, and at times this led to comical scenes where gangs of women would set upon a non-unionist, tear off his shirt and black-lead him.

The geological problems of the South Wales Coalfield were far greater than elsewhere in Britain. As a consequence conditions were more dangerous and it was more difficult to actually mine the coal. Some seams were less than three feet high, even down to eighteen inches or less in places, forcing colliers to work on their hands and knees, at times in mud and water. Cutting the rock above or below this seam was a complete waste of time, so the collier worked within the height of the seam all the time. There was hardly any room to swing the mandril. Firstly the coal was undercut at the bottom of the seam, and generally supported by props. For that, the collier would usually work on his side. The next

Coal-face, Big Pit
This shows the old style of coal-face working, with wooden props holding up the roof. The 'lurching' appearance of some of the props certainly heightens one's awareness of the dangers of working underground. In the foreground stands part of the conveyor belt, which had to be dismantled and carried forward as the face advanced. On the left I have sketched in Rhys, the ex-miner who sat explaining the operation in graphic detail.

Empty to-
Clydach Vale
Load 10 Tons
Tare 6-1-1

operation involved knocking out the props and hoping the weight of the roof would bring the coal down. In some hard seams explosives were used to weaken the coal. The coal-face advanced a few feet each day in this way, and the area behind the face allowed to collapse, apart from the roadways which had to be advanced along with the face. Extending the roads involved ripping away rock to create a larger tunnel, another dangerous task.

Because of the thinness of the Welsh coal seams, colliers thus did not, man for man, produce as much coal as their counterparts in other coalfields. This had a bad effect on their wages, which were paid for piecework. As conditions varied from day to day in the same location, the collier could never earn exactly the same each day. Complicated pay structures and regulations also made life difficult for the miner. Early in his career, Todd Jones experienced the iniquities perpetrated by the owners: 'The size of the coal produced was always checked, and if it was found to be too small you didn't get paid. But they still sold it – and at a higher price, see!'

Surface workers tended to earn less than their colleagues underground. The work was not nearly so demanding or dangerous. Apart from specialist workers such as blacksmiths and engineers, older workers and those that had been injured were normally given surface jobs, although there were instances of miners over seventy years of age still working underground, though these were employed on the easier jobs, and not on

previous page

Coal Train Passing Hetty Shaft

At the height of coal-mining in the valleys there was little opportunity for trains to go at any speed; on average it took up to twelve hours for a coal-train to get from the valley heads down to Cardiff Docks. This scene shows the later years, after all the buildings surrounding the Hetty engine house have been demolished. I found the 0–6–0 pannier tank engine throwing out all that steam at the Dean Forest Railway at Norchard. It was typical of the locomotives used on the valley lines.

hewing the coal. Archibald Eckley emphasizes the interdependence of their colleages: 'If you had a problem, a bad back perhaps, you had to wait for your butty [to help].'

The work was not without its humour. Working closely together in cramped, difficult and dangerous circumstances bred a strong camaraderie among the miners. Todd Jones recalls some of the many nicknames he encountered during his days at Cefn Coed: Dai Loose Head – 'he played loose-head prop in rugby'; Dai One-way – 'part-time driver of a hearse'; Dai Pumps – 'this Dai worked on the pumps'; Id Bach – 'Idris was short in stature'; Twm Tyrfa – 'Tom Thunder, he had a very loud voice'; Lew Coch – 'Lew was ginger-headed'. This system was extremely useful where so many miners had the same name, and the nickname varied according to where they came from, what they did, or even in some cases, what they looked like.

Sport, of course, was very important to the miners. Getting out on to a sports field after the cramped confines of the coalface must have felt like heaven. The South Wales mining community produced a number of boxing champions, and by the late nineteenth century football and rugby had become especially popular. Rugby particularly appealed to the miner, and by the beginning of the twentieth century it had become the national game, following the tremendous successes of the Welsh side.

For the miners' wives, however, life must have seemed to be one long drudge. The day started early, preparing breakfast for the men on the early shift, then preparing a bath for those coming off night shift. With youngsters going to school and the washing filthy with mine-dust, work continued throughout the day without break. The afternoon shift changeover would then involve further work, and so on. Despite the vast quantities of dirt being brought into the households they were kept amazingly clean. The women of the valleys took great pride in keeping their homes tidy, and this extended to scrubbing clean the flagstones outside.

In retrospect, attitudes of those days seem, at times, rather odd. Comfortable chairs were thought of as indicating weakness, and scoffed at by those brought up on hard living. Clothes too, attracted derision in some instances: men seen wearing shoes instead of boots, for example, were considered effeminate, yet young boys were dressed in frocks even as late as 1913! Shawls were very common for carrying babies around. On Sundays a complete transformation came over the miners when they would be seen out in their Sunday best, especially at chapel or when singing. In fact, the onlooker would have found it difficult to tell if they were miners or not.

Despite the zealous approach to cleanliness, the congested cottages with poor sanitary arrangements led to epidemics of typhoid fever, typhus and cholera in places. In the late nineteenth century a government inspector found the Rhondda had rivers containing large amounts of human excrement, horse and pig manure and entrails from the slaughterhouses, among other

right

Winter Sunlight, Celynen North Colliery
This colliery, at Newbridge, was sunk in 1913, and coal was produced from the Black Vein, Meadow Vein and Old Coal Seams. It was closed in 1985.

things. Open sewers and polluted water supplies exacerbated illness. Infant mortality was at times desperately high – over 20 per cent in some areas. Poor diet made matters worse. Even so, many of the families who had moved from a country existence felt their lifestyle had improved considerably: in the valleys there were better shops, more social events and eventually even such things as electric lighting. And, of course, at the Co-op customers received a dividend when they bought goods, so that in a time of need they could draw out their 'divis'.

In conditions of deprivation a tremendous community spirit flourished, something that is almost impossible to find in places where there have been no shared hardships. Nowhere was this more pronounced than in the valley communities. In the nineteenth century there was no social security system to fall back on in times of poverty. Illness, accident, lock-out, unemployment or just old age created horrendous hardships. Families developed an inter-dependence at times like that, setting up soup kitchens, relying on help from friends and relations, and even scraping for coal on the waste tips. This was not just for their own use, but to sell even though it was illegal. Failing all else, the poverty-struck could apply for help from the Poor Law Authorities, and this generally meant going into the workhouse, an exceedingly harsh regime. Many workers, in anticipation of difficult periods, joined Friendly Societies, paying a weekly subscription. In return for this they would receive financial assistance during hard times.

With the growth of these communities, chapels sprang up at quite a pace. By the middle of the nineteenth century the Church of England had lost favour with much of the Welsh population. Nonconformist chapels exerted a powerful influence over life in the mining communities, and from this grew choirs, bands, eisteddfodau and other activities. Many of the social events and pastimes were centred around the chapels, and for most it provided the only outlet for people to express themselves through the arts. Some chapels organized events every night of the week, so it is easy to realize how choirs became so popular and important in the valleys. Huge crowds of chapel-goers would be drawn by well-known visiting preachers, on occasion causing large queues and even forcing the congregation to spill outside. Outings to the seaside – usually Porthcawl or Barry Island – were often the highlight of the summer, and these were usually arranged by the chapels.

To a large extent chapels also became instrumental in keeping alive the Welsh language. With such large immigration into South Wales, especially in Monmouthshire, Welsh became very diluted. In addition to this, company policy strongly discouraged its use, even to the extent of dismissing workers heard speaking it. However, the further west one travelled through the coalfield, the more Welsh became evident.

Challenging the chapels as a focal point, the other buildings to stand out in the valley towns are the miners' institutes. Their imposing façades still stand as reminders to their days of glory, yet

Abercynon Miners' Institute

The institute was opened on 19 September 1904, and stands at the top of a steep street. The row of cottages, each with a tall chimney, leads the eye up to the institute, with its architectural style so typical of valley institutes.

many are now undergoing a second lease of life as arts centres. In the main they were funded by deductions from the wages of miners, but many of the more benevolent coal-owners paid a contribution. Apart from providing a place for meetings, games and a social centre for the mining communities, the institutes also contained libraries from which many acquired their main education.

By 1913 the Rhondda was at the height of its output, with well over fifty deep mines and some 41,000 miners. At this time the Eastern Valley of Monmouthshire boasted around forty working pits. In the whole of South Wales the mining industry employed almost 250,000 workers, and produced some 57 million tons of coal per annum. As Britain went to war in 1914, the South Wales Coalfield was at its peak. The demand for steam coal for the Royal Navy increased, but output suffered with the conscription of so many miners into the armed forces. Disputes between the miners and the coal-owners continued, as it appeared that the owners were making record profits. By the end of the First World War output was well down. The war at sea had seriously disrupted the export market, and the first signs of cutting down on production were becoming evident.

Here Be Dragons

The phantom lurks, his evil breath
rolls its shapeless clouds of death,
spreads through tunnels, poisons, smothers
singing birds with yellow feathers.

Sharp the tang of coal and damp,
chill shadows run before the lamp
and darkness threatens, presses round,
swallows air, absorbing sound –

the rasp of ancient earth's raw cough,
echoes rattle, infirm rock
groans a warning, muffled, deep –
the monster stamps his blackened feet

and tremors travel, wave on wave
through passages and flooded caves,
to conjure legends roused from sleep
in hellish halls, primeval, bleak.

From nameless regions underground
a growling tide of hungry sound
surges and revives sheer dread –
the giant leaves his stony bed

with splitting seam, the spitting rock
showers downwards and the shock
scatters men, they run and shout
and scramble, frantic to get out.

Worming through a crumbling shaft
they gasp for air – a thin cool draught
that filters into nightmare worlds
where faith deserts and fear uncurls

its superstitious tongue and claws,
and shivers while it digs and gnaws -
for here be dragons, jealous, cruel,
guarding hoards of fossil fuel.

JEAN M. THOMAS

CHAPTER THREE

Hardships, Protests and Disasters

During the latter half of the nineteenth century and early twentieth, some horrific disasters occurred in many pits of the coalfield. On 8 November 1867, 178 miners perished in the Ferndale pit in Rhondda Fach, the largest loss to that date in the whole of the coalfield. Even that was dwarfed by the disaster eleven years later in the Prince of Wales Colliery at Abercarn in Monmouthshire. This pit was sunk in 1865 by the Ebbw Vale Mining Company, and soon became very productive. Around midday on Wednesday 11 September 1878 a tremendous explosion resounded around the valley, startling the inhabitants for miles. A dense column of acrid smoke rose from the shaft, engulfing the winding gear and followed by flames. The whole community dropped whatever they were doing. Grabbing coats and shawls, they set off for the pit, quickly jamming the approach roads in their haste to get news.

Doors at the top of the upcast shaft had been badly damaged by the explosion, rendering the ventilation system virtually useless, as the fan simply sucked in fresh air instead of foul air from the pit. The first task was to repair the doors so that the gas and foul air could be drawn out. An unknown colliery worker then took charge in the absence of Mr Pond the colliery manager, and recalled: 'Knowing that no man could live in that pit in the state that it then was with smoke and sulphur coming up the two pits, I at once commenced to close these doors on the top of the upcast shaft, they being blowed open. I called out that there was some planks wanted to cover over the top of the pit and some Bradish cloth from the stores.'

Underground Junction, Big Pit

This scene shows a junction not far from the pit bottom, where there is some overhead lighting. The shapes of the tunnels and texture on the stonework excited me, and although there were coal drams around, they were not quite in the right place. In this painting, therefore, I have 'imported' a dram from elsewhere to add further interest.

Once this was done, he initiated a descent into the smoky downcast shaft on the double-decker pit cage. 'We descended down the pit very steady, stopping occasionally to see that all was safe, I being the signal man to give the signal to stop or to go on. William Simmonds was on the bottom deck watching that all things was right underneath, and I was on the top deck with a sledgehammer to strike on the coursing of the cage and to watch the sides of the pit that there was nothing hanging. Charlie

Morgans was with me on the top deck. The others was with Billy on the bottom deck. We did not find anything to stop the progress of the cage until we got to the top of the wood conductors in the bottom of the pit. One of them was shifted so as to stop the cage from going any lower. When we saw that we could go no further I gave the signal to stop the cage. I got off on the pump side and climbed, Charlie Morgans with me, down about twelve feet to a biat and we assisted those men up to the cage. I had to climb that cage every time that I went to the bottom of the pit.'

At the bottom a number of miners had gathered, many severely burned and injured. These were helped on to the cage which then began carrying up the survivors. Moving along the roadways, the dim lights of the rescuers pierced through the smoky atmosphere to reveal dead bodies lying everywhere – the charred, shapeless forms of the loved ones of those hurrying to the pit-head above. Some were dying. The force of the blast had hurled drams along the roadways, like leaves in a gale. Among the carnage and debris lay the bodies of horses. In places the coal and timber supports were on fire, and as well as the gory mounds the rescuers had to contend with deadly afterdamp, the toxic fumes caused by the explosion. For several hours they struggled in the most appallingly desperate conditions in an attempt to find any of their comrades who might still be alive in the maze of workings.

By evening, with conditions underground deteriorating, and with the strong possibility of a further explosion, the rescuers, close to exhaustion, were recalled. Those waiting at the pit-head for news had to endure a long night. An inspection the following morning found that fires were still raging and there was a continuing build-up of gas, making it lethal to descend the shaft. Eventually the decision was made to flood the mine with water from the nearby Monmouthshire canal, much to the distress of those with loved ones still missing.

The pit was virtually destroyed, with roof-falls blocking much of the roadways. The majority of the bodies remained entombed in its bowels. In total 268 miners died. Ninety-three were rescued, but of these six died. Reluctantly the mine had to be abandoned. Years later the mine was reopened with new workings. William Simmonds was among those commended for bravery.

By far the worst mining disaster to happen in Wales occurred at the Universal Colliery, Senghenydd, a pit owned by Lewis Merthyr Consolidated Collieries Ltd. It was a very dangerous pit, well-known for harbouring lethal gas. On 24 May 1901 a violent explosion tore through the mine, killing eighty-two colliers – a terrible taste of what was to come twelve years later.

In the early hours of the morning of Tuesday 14 October 1913 some 950 miners began a descent of nearly 2,000 feet into the pit. With such a huge workforce it naturally took some time for everyone to reach their workplace. A cruel twist of irony ensured that fate waited for all to be present before a violent explosion rent the mine just after 8 a.m. So fierce was the blast that it hurled the cage up the Lancaster shaft and smashed it into the winding gear with tremendous force. Black smoke billowed out of the

David Bellamy

stricken mine. A rescue team of night-shift miners led by colliery manager Edward Shaw descended the York shaft, in a slow descent through smoke and fumes.

Progress through the mine was hampered by fires – in places the rescuers were beaten back by flames with the ferocity of a furnace. With the roof supports on fire it would not be long before the roof itself collapsed. Timber was cracking and falling and the heat was intense. Dying men lay beside overturned coal drams, some trying to chalk messages to their loved ones on the sides. Mine Rescue Teams arrived from the Rhymney Valley, from Crumlin, Porth and further afield, bringing with them breathing apparatus. But even these devices were useless against the ferocity of fire and dense smoke. One of the rescuers was killed when the roof caved in. Nightfall came, and still survivors were being brought up, each arrival at bank being greeted by cheers from the waiting crowd. By evening, thousands waited around the pit. The next morning saw the continuation of the struggle to find survivors. When some of the roof-falls were cleared more miners were found still alive, though some had lost consciousness.

Volunteers arrived from all parts, even from as far afield as London, but there was little they could do. By Thursday all hope was abandoned of finding anyone else alive. Almost every family in Senghenydd had lost a relative. About ninety of the bodies were so badly mutilated that they could not be identified. Altogether the death roll amounted to 439 men and boys – the

left

Senghenydd

A small memorial to the disaster of 1913, when 439 miners lost their lives in the Universal Colliery, now stands in Senghenydd. In the distance, at the head of the village the spoil heaps from the pit can be seen, now mainly overgrown with grass.

worst disaster in the history of coal-mining in Britain. But for the superhuman efforts of the rescue teams this toll would have been much higher. In the inquiry that followed, the probable cause of the explosion was thought to be ignition of accumulated gas by electrical signalling equipment, though as with most of the explosions, no one could be absolutely certain of the actual cause. Typical of the injustice found in coal-mining history, the pit manager took the rap, while the owners who laid down the rules for the mine got away almost scot-free.

But it was not just dramatic pit explosions that claimed the lives of colliers. On every shift they faced death and injury through roof-falls, flooding from sudden inrushes of water, or accidents underground. No matter how careful the miner, if luck was against him there was no way he could survive. Yet miners developed a sixth sense, listening for creaking timber supports that gave warning of impending disaster, and watching for movement in the rock strata. Hugh Lewis of Resolven recalls an incident in Blaengwrach Colliery when a sharp-eyed colliery official spotted a slight movement in the roof supports of the six-foot seam. He immediately hurried the men out of the area, only to see the steel arches suddenly slide forward like dominoes as the roof caved in. Luckily, everyone escaped on that occasion.

Buckling Girders, Taff Merthyr

Some miners suffered dreadful injuries. Mrs Annie Gough of Pantygasseg relates how her brother George who worked at Blaenserchan Colliery was kicked in the leg by a pit pony at the age of seventeen. After a time of doubt he had his foot amputated. Sadly this did not put things right and he had to have a bit more of his leg taken off. In all he had no less than four amputations. 'He ended up with two artificial limbs – one for working down the pit, and one for best.'

As well as accidents, disease took a heavy toll on those who worked underground. It took a long time before pneumoconiosis and silicosis – diseases caused by inhaling dust – were recognized as industrial diseases. When miners complained about dust, management would even at times reply that it was 'good for you', or 'it cures heartburn!' Todd Jones carried out many safety investigations on behalf of the union and remembers one miner who for some time complained of having silicosis, but the doctor insisted it was asthma. When the miner died his lungs were found to be full of dust 'as hard as concrete'. Coal-dust also entered open wounds and formed the characteristic 'blue scars' common among miners. Miners would carry iodine ampules in case of injury. The glass was broken when needed and the iodine allowed to soak into a cotton wool pad for application to the wound.

Another disease prevalent in the mines was nystagmus, a condition which weakened the eyes, and in extreme cases could cause giddiness and black-outs. This was brought on by long periods of eye-strain from the poor light of the safety lamps or flickering candles. With accidents, explosions, roof-falls, hard labour and disease, it is little wonder that around the turn of the century some people equated the collier's work with enforced hard labour in prison.

Appalling safety conditions in the mines caused numerous strikes. In the summer of 1910 the extreme difficulty in working a new seam at the Ely Colliery in Tonypandy brought things to a head when negotiations between the miners and management of the owners, the giant Cambrian Combine, broke down. The amount of stone present in the seam contributed to a lot of unproductive work, which in effect meant that the colliers worked longer for less reward. On 1 September 1910 all Ely miners were locked out by management for not agreeing to their terms. Within two months the other pits in the Cambrian Combine were out on strike. On 7 November miners and police clashed violently at a large protest meeting outside the Glamorgan Colliery at Llwynpia. Even with imported police, Captain Lionel Lindsay, the chief constable of Glamorgan, felt the need for reinforcements, and requested the government to send in troops.

The following night, after a further clash with police outside the Glamorgan Colliery, the crowd began to smash shop windows and ransack the place. The police contingent was virtually powerless and soon the main street was strewn with all sorts of goods. Only one shop escaped the carnage, that of Willie

right

Marine Colliery, Cwm
The Ebbw Vale Steel, Iron and Coal Company sank Marine Colliery in 1889. On St Davids Day, 1 March 1927, a horrific explosion ignited by firedamp rent the mine, the fire further fuelled by suspended coal-dust. Fifty-two miners were killed that day. Exactly one hundred years after sinking the colliery it was finally closed. The winding gear was brought down on 8 November 1990, removing the remains of the last colliery in the Ebbw Fawr.

David Bellamy

Pit-head, Tower Colliery

Llewellyn who had contributed to Wales' 1905 victory over the All-Blacks! Winston Churchill, the Home Secretary, ordered in the 18th Hussars and several infantry units. The Hussars were billeted at Pontypridd.

The arrival of troops quietened down the situation, but their involvement on the instructions of Churchill was a contentious issue never forgotten in the valleys. Various explanations for the Tonypandy Riots have been aired, but perhaps the most convincing is the argument that it was a backlash against the shop-owning fraternity who were deemed to be on the side of the coal-owners and police.

With widespread disasters and fatal accidents set against a background of complete indifference to safety considerations on the part of the coal-owners, together with the owners' hostility towards trade unions, the coalfield was seething with unrest. Add to this the policies of the owners of the Cambrian Combine, as the First World War approached, and it is easy to see why there was so much antagonism towards the authorities.

During the First World War the government took over the running of the coalfields to ensure that there would be no further strikes to hinder the war effort. Once the war ended a Royal Commission was set up to consider the possibility of nationalizing the coal industry. This was not because of any socialist tendencies of the government, but because of the obvious need for better cooperation between miners and management. Coal was a vital national resource, and many felt that it was in the best interests of the State to take over the mines. Although the commission's report was in favour of nationalization, the government in 1921 handed back the mines to the coal-owners. In South Wales wages were cut. The owners stated that wage levels had increased too much while the government had controlled the coalfields, and those miners who refused to accept lower wages – in many grades this amounted to 50 per cent less – would be sacked. On 1 April 1921 miners throughout the country were locked out. For three months they waited for support from the transport workers, but it never came. The miners were forced to return to work on the owners' terms.

Coal production increased temporarily, but by the end of the decade exports from South Wales had fallen from a peak of nearly

Penrhiwceiber Colliery

The colliery, situated near Mountain Ash, is seen here looking north-west in evening light. It was sunk between 1872 and 1878, and the owners referred to it in the anglicized form of Penrikyber.

one-third of the world's coal exports to a mere 3 per cent. The war had had a savage effect on the coal industry, and because of the geological problems Welsh coal was more costly to mine than that of any other region in Britain. Many of the smaller companies folded up. Some of the least productive mines were closed, and in 1925 miners were not only asked to accept further cuts in their wages, but to work an extra hour on their shift. In April 1926 British coal-mines once again ground to a standstill as the miners were locked out for refusing to take cuts in pay. This time the Trade Union Congress backed the miners and a General Strike began on 3 May 1926. This lasted nine days, when the TUC called off the strike and the miners were left to battle on alone.

Unlike other coalfields, in South Wales the struggle against those attempting to return to work grew extremely bitter. On occasion, up to sixty policemen would escort three or four 'blacklegs' on their way to and from work. Police were imported from other areas in an endeavour not only to keep the peace, but to break the strike. Not only were blacklegs ambushed, even in lorries, but often police reinforcements responding to a call for help would be ambushed themselves, for feelings were running

Celynen South Colliery

Three shafts were begun in 1873, two for winding coal and the third for ventilation. By 1876 coal was being raised and by the turn of the century the pit employed around 1,700 men and some 200 horses. The colliery was closed in 1985.

Here I have vignetted the foreground to lose superfluous detail (a school playing field). The trees have been made to frame the mine detail, and with so much detail, the sky has been kept simple.

high against the police. Surprisingly, there was a high proportion of women in these attacks. In hard times of severe unemployment, as later in 1992–3, highly organized gangs would raid coal-yards and outcrop areas to obtain coal for selling commercially. All this irregular activity and strong police presence gave the coalfield the appearance of a battlefield in places.

The mining communities were now fighting for survival. Soup kitchens were set up in chapels, institutes or wherever possible. Parcels of food were distributed to the needy, and boot centres organized, for so many children went barefoot to school. Many countries sent parcels of goods. It was not until the end of 1926 that the miners again were forced back to work by starvation. Militants were thrown out, never to work again in the coal industry. Apart from the anthracite coalfield in West Wales, unemployment became a major problem in the valleys. Many emigrated to the English towns in search of work. Those that remained during the Depression somehow managed to find ways of surviving and keeping up morale. Jazz and Character Bands began to appear, providing a carnival atmosphere to the valleys. James Jones reckoned that there were around 120 such bands in the Rhondda alone, providing quite a spectacle. Competitions were an incentive to keep the standards high. It was not all doom and gloom; the tremendous community spirit never faltered.

Feeling ran strong in the valleys. Mass unemployment, company unionism based on a no-strike principle, unwelcome visits by the British Union of Fascists and, at times, hostile journalism, all contributed to an anger that often spilled over into violence. Hunger marches characterized by huge processions were arranged, with over 60,000 people attending some of the meetings in the valleys. By 1932 male unemployment stood at 44 per cent in Wales. Tuberculosis became rife. Families foraged for coal wherever possible, on the mountain-tops and around the pits. Mrs Annie Gough remembers one episode in particular. 'My father and brother were digging by the side of the house for coal. They got the posts up lovely, but when it came to, they hit water. It was spring water, so we piped it into a barrel. From then on we had lots of lovely water, but no coal!'

Once again, on the outbreak of the Second World War, the government took over the running of the coalfields. Afterwards, when Labour was swept into power they took the step of nationalizing the industry, and on 1 January 1947 the National Coal Board was born. This was greatly welcomed by the miners. Immediately funds were made available to modernize the industry so that it could compete on better terms with the coal industries of other countries. Germany in particular had much more efficient mines than Britain. Gone were the days of picks and shovels. Coal-cutting machines and power-loaders were introduced. The use of conveyor belts to transport coal from the coal-faces and down the roadways was improved. One of the most revolutionary advances was the introduction of hydraulic pit-props to replace timber. The hydraulic props could be put in position in a mere thirty seconds, a tremendous improvement.

Six Bells Colliery, Abertillery

The Arail Griffin Colliery at Six Bells was sunk during the 1890s, and on the eve of the First World War had a manpower of 2,857. At 10.45 a.m. on Monday 28 June 1960 an explosion occurred in the W District of the Old Coal Seam. The effect of the explosion was felt in Brynmawr, six miles away. Forty-five miners died. Six Bells was closed in 1988.

Conveyor Belt, Taff Merthyr

This shows an incomplete section of a second conveyor coming in from the left to drop coal on to the one running along the main roadway.

Many of these advances brought about by nationalization considerably improved pit safety, particularly at the coal-face where colliers could now cut coal beneath a solid steel canopy. Electric cap-lamps were introduced, greatly improving both safety and efficiency. Other safety refinements included sprinkling stone dust over the roadways to render the coal-dust inert, and also the introduction of water barriers. Accidents were reduced by around two-thirds of the rate prior to 1947. The whole industry was transformed. During the 1960s piecework was abolished and a uniform wage introduced. However, this badly affected production and so a bonus system linked to productivity had to be negotiated.

With the vast improvements in safety by the 1960s, it was a stunned world that received the news of the disaster in October 1966. At 9.15 on the grey morning of Friday 21st the massive Tip No. 7 containing thousands of tons of waste from the Merthyr Vale Colliery began to slide down the mountainside like black lava. Slowly it slithered towards the village of Aberfan, engulfing all in its path. Lessons had just started in Pantglas Junior School when the sea of slurry and coal waste burst into the classrooms and tore away parts of the school. Young lives were snuffed out like candles. The hideous black ooze engulfed two classrooms and smashed through others, then broke out on the lower side. Some children in classrooms at the front of the school managed to clamber out of windows, but most stood no chance, being totally engulfed in the morass. Within minutes 144 people were buried alive; 116 of them were children. Miners rushed from all over South Wales to join in the rescue with the emergency services.

The eyes of the world were focussed on Aberfan. Donations poured in from forty countries, and the fund rose to almost £2 million. The official tribunal ruled that the National Coal Board was entirely responsible for the disaster. Minor slides had occurred in earlier years, and warnings had been given by the local council. The tips were removed, but the Labour government raised embittered feelings by taking £150,000 from the disaster fund to foot the bill for the removal.

overleaf

Merthyr Vale Colliery

John Nixon sunk the shafts from 1869 to 1875 with great difficulty because of sudden intakes of water. Sinkers had many narrow escapes as a result of shafts flooding rapidly. It was the spoil heaps from this Merthyr Vale colliery that were responsible for the Aberfan disaster in October 1966. The pit was closed in 1989.

David Bellamy

CHAPTER FOUR

The Rundown of the Coalfield

The swinging sixties unfortunately brought little cheer to the coal industry in South Wales in a decade of gloom. Not only did Aberfan cast a shadow across the coalfield, but two other disasters brought home the ever-present threat to those who worked the seams: in 1960 forty-five men were killed in an explosion at Six Bells Colliery in Abertillery, and in 1965 the Cambrian Colliery disaster claimed thirty-one lives. Added to the misery was the acceleration of pit closures. From 1955 onwards pits began to close more frequently. When the Labour government was elected in 1964 the industry expected some reprieve from this sad state of affairs, but their hopes were dashed. No less than seventy-four

Pantygasseg Private Mine

I couldn't resist painting this marvellous scene in the private drift mine near Pantygasseg, with the amazing collection of buildings.

Tower Colliery from Ffyndaff Opencast Site
From this spot, part-way down into the bowels of the opencast site, an excellent view was obtained on the contrast between deep and opencast mining. The opencast is almost at the door of Tower Colliery.

deep mines were closed in South Wales alone during the 1960s, decimating the coalfield. Most of these pits had coal left – vast reserves in some cases – but they were deemed to be 'uneconomic' against a background of cheap oil and the importation of subsidized coal.

By 1971 the market for coal had changed dramatically from the days of battleships and steam railways, with over half the coal produced going into electricity generation. The coal strike in 1972 therefore suddenly revealed with dramatic effect how vulnerable power supplies were to industrial action. By picketing railways and power stations instead of the pits, the miners held the trump card, forcing the government to acquiesce to their demand for improved wages on a parity with workers in other industries. In 1974 similar tactics by striking miners eventually led to the toppling of the Conservative government. With huge increases in the price of oil, the coal industry enjoyed a period of revival for the rest of the decade.

The domination of the coal market by the electricity generators increased at the beginning of the 1980s. In the meantime the lessons of the 1972 and 1974 strikes had been examined by the new Conservative government. As a consequence, coal began to be stockpiled at power stations, with the prime minister taking a personal interest in progress. Contingency plans were also made to import more coal and to introduce dual coal and oil-firing into the power stations. Money was poured into the development of nuclear powered stations. In 1984 one of the most bitter and lengthy of all miners' strikes broke out. Clearly the power of the miners haunted the Conservative government. Did one side or the other actually plan a showdown on such a massive scale? The level of violence, mass picketing and policing on a scale never before seen in Britain tore the coalfields apart, especially in Yorkshire. In South Wales the strike was fairly solid and certainly did not reach the scale of violence seen in South Yorkshire and Nottinghamshire. At Deep Navigation Colliery coachloads of miners on their way to work were turned back, not by hundreds of massed pickets, but by little Dai on his own!

The 1984–5 strike was not about pay. It concerned the closure of twenty further pits and hence the future of the industry. Miners

right

Stormy Night, Tower Colliery

Tower Colliery is the last remaining deep mine in the South Wales Coalfield, and unlike the other pits featured in this book, is situated on wide open terrain near Hirwaun. The depth of the shaft is less than 200 feet, with the coal routed out via a drift further east on the mountainside.

were fighting for their jobs. The strike was characterized by strong direct action by the miners' wives. They arranged events to support the striking miners, from jumble sales to sponsored walks. Thousands of women turned up at rallies and marched behind their banner 'Women Against Pit Closures'. They organized food parcels and even appeared alongside the men on the picket lines. Many womens' groups formed close bonds with other towns and cities. In March 1984 a group from Maerdy went to Oxford, and there they stayed for the rest of the strike. The Oxford Miners' Support Group was formed and raised a considerable amount of finance to feed the miners.

Public support varied, as did that of fellow trade unionists. It would no doubt have been stronger had a national ballot taken place by the National Union of Mineworkers. Why did they not hold a ballot? To the average person this appeared undemocratic. Classic tactics of dividing the miners held the key: the National Coal Board had invested heavily in the Nottinghamshire pits, and the miners there were given high productivity bonuses. Other areas by comparison were under the threat of closure. Had a ballot been held most of the large Nottinghamshire coalfield would have voted against striking. This was the fundamental reasoning behind the no-ballot policy. The miners stood alone, confronting the whole might of the British establishment in their fight to keep their jobs. The media concentrated on the violent scenes. Showing picketing miners playing football with the police was not 'hot' news. Running battles between pickets and police occurred even in the pit villages, away from the industrial sites. Innocent people were sucked into the brutal conflict and miner was set against miner. Orwell's *1984* seemed to have been prophetic. The cost was enormous, in both financial terms and those of human relations.

On the cold frosty morning of 5 March 1985 the miners returned to work, having lost their battle. At dawn a long procession left Maerdy village and wound its way up the mountain road towards the pit, led by the brass band. Maerdy miners proudly marched back to their pit. But it was not just the mining industry that had lost: the communities, the politicians, the legal authorities, and even the government were worse off. Much of the brutal cost had yet to come. In July 1985 only thirty-one pits remained in the South Wales area. The National Coal Board changed its name to British Coal, but the butchery of the industry continued. Yet why should we mourn the passing of an industry that has taken such a cruel toll on the lives of so many? Despite the hardship and danger, almost every miner prefers to be working down his pit than to be on the dole. These feelings were reinforced when we witnessed the closing of the last pit in the Rhondda.

A damp drizzle clung to the mountain slopes at the head of the Rhondda Fach, with

Lewis Merthyr Pit-head

deep puddles lying across the broken, pot-holed track that led up the mountainside to Maerdy Colliery. The all-pervading gloom of that December morning in 1990 reflected the atmosphere at the mine where a huge crowd had gathered to witness the closing of the last pit in the Rhondda Valley. Hours before the great wheels of the pit-head gear had stopped turning, and now stood statuesque above the unfolding scene. Dignitaries spoke, hymns and carols were sung, and children recited poetry. The colliery band then struck up 'Cwm Rhondda', and hardened miners fought to hold back the tears of overpowering feelings. An intense sadness cut through everyone like a knife. This was the end of an era: after nearly 150 years the mighty Rhondda, which at one time boasted some fifty-three pits, no longer produced coal. Gareth Childs, secretary of the Rhondda branch of NALGO, expressed the sentiments of the union: 'If there was any justice in the world, the last pit in the world to close would be in the Rhondda.' The dignitaries, the miners, their families and supporters formed up behind the union banner and for the last time, in that uncompromising valleys drizzle, marched down the sad track into Maerdy itself, where lines of chimneys reflected starkly on the wet roofs.

In the late 1980s that scene had been enacted many times in the valleys of Gwent and Glamorgan; for in the whole of the British coal industry nowhere has seen such a dramatic slide in fortunes as that of the South Wales Coalfield. The pride of the

right

Closure of Maerdy Pit, Rhondda Fach
Maerdy was the last pit to close in the Rhondda Valley, and the scene here depicts that gloomy, wet day in December 1990 when the miners, their families and supporters left the mine for the very last time. Maerdy produced some legendary miners' union leaders, such as Arthur Horner and Noah Ablett.

N.U.M.
MAERDY LODGE

miners – a pride in their work, their mine and their comradeship – is something which perhaps outsiders find almost impossible to grasp, especially those in Whitehall; and it is one of the strongest reasons for miners wanting to save their pits.

With the number of mines diminishing rapidly I felt under pressure to capture the atmosphere of working underground before it was too late. British Coal agreed to my request for an underground visit, and on a beautiful spring morning I found myself descending the shaft into the stygian depths of Taff Merthyr Colliery. My guide was training officer Lee Jones who had worked seven years underground. He warned me that the walk to the coal-face from pit bottom was three and a half miles, and to keep me alert related how someone had fallen 1,300 feet down the shaft only a few weeks before. Being over six feet tall I was at a disadvantage, forever banging my helmet against the overhead girder system used for transporting equipment, usually in boxes, affectionately known as 'coffins'.

Our route led along a wide roadway, with a noisy conveyor belt on one side carrying the coal towards pit bottom. The dust-covered floor was uneven and littered with all manner of debris, punctuated in places with mud, while above hung the girder system. At times we changed course and ducked down under the conveyor belt. At all times our passing was accompanied by a strong, warm air current from behind. This ventilated the roadway, but blew a lot of coal-dust about, contributing to my blackened features. Coal-dust clung with a glutinous consistency

Main Roadway, Taff Merthyr

Here the conveyor belt carrying the coal to pit bottom is seen to the right, with the overhead girder system clearly visible.

to the perspiration running down our faces. The inky blackness stretched uninterrupted for ages at times. Then dim lights could be made out in the distance, gradually getting closer, as miners approached. Lee greeted everyone with a jovial and friendly banter. I seized each opportunity to sketch rapidly while Lee talked. Subjects varied from the miners themselves to pieces of equipment or the general scene. Moving images of miners caught in the beams of their cap-lamps were especially evocative but the most difficult and frustrating of all to capture on paper, because of the need for speed. At a repair holt, where two contractors were repairing the walls and roof, I paused to sketch. They were repairing a really bad patch which had been subject to 'squeezing' – the closing up of roadways and workings because of pressure

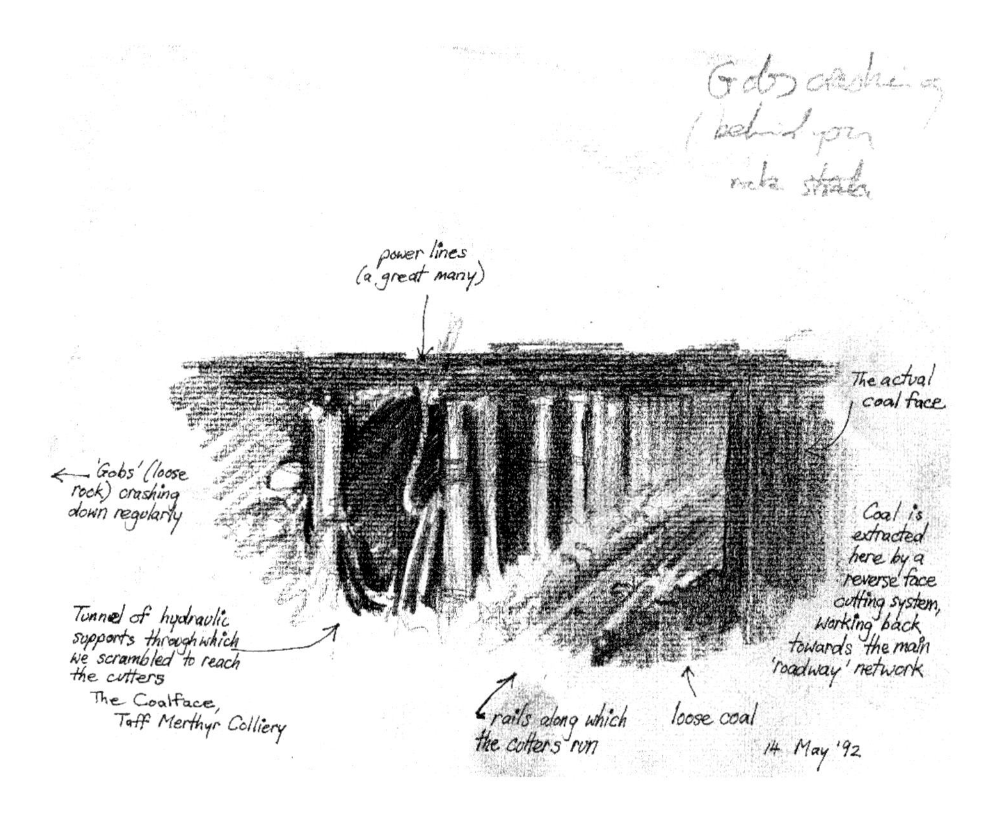

Coal-face, Taff Merthyr

In this instance, the original sketch has been left as it stands, only I have added explanations in writing around the edges. If this is not done fairly soon afterwards, a lot of valuable information can be lost. Studying the sketch can trigger very clear recollections at times.

from above or at the sides. Squeezing is generally a gradual process, but now and then a roof can cave in without warning, crushing everything in seconds. Twisted support girders on one side brought the message home very graphically.

With constant sketching stops it took us nearly two hours to reach the actual coal-face. Here we found the colliers having their lunch-break, unable to work because of the high level of the gas content in the air. Not even the conveyor belt was operating, and this made the place seem eerily silent. One of the miners volunteered to pose while I sketched him operating a machine, to the accompaniment of jeers and jokes from his butties, with several references to the size of paper required to sketch his head.

Beyond our position of comparative safety a fairly regular crashing of falling rock and coal – or gobs, as they are known underground – could be heard. We then crawled through a low tunnel of hydraulic roof supports for what seemed to be almost a quarter of a mile, having to scramble over the occasional old box and oil-drum until we reached the cutting machine. One of the cutter-men tried to start it up to show me the operation, but it refused to budge, apart from shooting out water-jets like some recumbent whale. We moved on to another cutter, and here it worked, the great metal teeth whirling at the same time as the water-jets. For some time I sat and sketched the machines which were covered in a thick layer of dust that dropped off at the edges

Starting the Cutter, Taff Merthyr
The gaps between the hydraulic supports have been deliberately lengthened so that more of the actual coal-cutting machine can be seen. In the picture the water jets have already started operating.

to reveal the odd patch of detail here and there. Then I was shown the operation of the hydraulic supports, and was amazed at the power, pushing the canopy up or down as directed. As the face advances, the fully automated hydraulic canopy holding up the roof moves forward with the cutting machines. The coal is dropped directly onto a conveyor belt.

Soon we were on our way back towards pit bottom, deviating from our outward route near the end to return via an FSV roadway. FSVs – Free Steered Vehicles – carried the coal out from the end of the conveyor belt, on its journey to the Aberthaw Power Station. In one place the roof jutted downwards with buckled girders showing evidence of powerful pressure from above. I hurried past the threatening contortions to where it was well-lit and uncluttered, enabling us to move faster. It did not take long to reach the pit bottom and we soon emerged once more into glorious sunlight.

On the surface I was amazed to see they still kept a budgerigar. Over the years budgies have been taken down the mines to detect gas; budgies are more likely to keel over first, and so give warning of gas. The birds are revived with oxygen. More sophisticated methods were evident in the surface control-room: computers monitor the levels of gas, as well as controlling other functions. When someone was asked how many men worked underground, the reply came back with typical colliery humour, 'about half of them!' The true answer was 368. All Taff Merthyr coal went to Aberthaw Power Station.

The visit had been important to me, not just from the point of view of obtaining sketches, but in order to gain a greater understanding of what was involved. The hard, uncompromising work underground where each man was reliant on his mate, bred a comradeship unmatched in most jobs. The humour of those underground had shone through, a humour that must be almost as important as the comradeship in helping the miners come to terms with, at times, horrendous situations.

Taff Merthyr was expecting to close in the not-too-distant future, but it was quite a shock when the news broke out on 13 October 1992 that of the three remaining mines in South Wales, Taff Merthyr and Betws Colliery on the western edge of the coalfield were to be axed almost immediately, along with twenty-nine pits from other areas, in the wholesale scrapping of the industry.

The *Alice in Wonderland* style political kicking around of the British Coal industry in the late 1980s and early '90s has assumed bizarre proportions, at times bordering on panic: the race to build more expensive gas-fired power stations, investment in overseas mining companies, the building of costly port facilities for the importation of coal, the importation of French electricity, and the rude haste with which privatization of British Coal is sought, are all evidence of this. With a total demise of the British Coal industry the country would be open to blackmail from abroad, left helpless by political manipulation. The pit closure announcement caused a furore in the country, so much so that the government

overleaf

Blaenserchan Colliery
Blaenserchan Colliery was sunk by Partridge, Jones and Company in 1890, high on a mountainside near Pontypool. The pit was connected to Tirpentwys and Hafodyrynys Collieries, where the coal was brought out after 1969. Blaenserchan was the last mine to work in the Eastern Valley of Gwent. I returned to the site after it had been demolished, to find it just a sad heap of rubble on the wide mountain ledge. Rusting wire hawsers wound like bindweed around posts, lumps of shattered concrete and the remains of conveyor belts. Not only was it a sad end to the pit, but it left a beautiful hillside and valley choking with debris.

David Bellamy

had to back down and promise to set up a coal review before closing a further single pit.

The British coal industry is one of the most efficient in Europe, yet this is clouded by the subsidization of foreign coal industries and the uneven playing field in the UK, whereby nuclear power is so heavily subsidized. With no coherent energy strategy, the coal industry is doomed to decline. With the loss of each colliery thousands of jobs go in the rail and service industries, and, particularly in the valleys of South Wales, there is hardly any alternative to the dole. Social repercussions have been totally ignored by those in power. It can only be a matter of time before Tower Colliery, the last deep mine in South Wales, is closed for ever.

The dramatic pit-head gear – the most powerful reminder that you are in a coalfield – has rapidly disappeared from the valleys. A few remain as memorials to the efforts of miners past, their wheels now stilled and silent save for the wind whistling through the spokes. Some feel they are better gone, scars that once blotted the landscape. Yet in many situations they evoke a haunting beauty, fitting well into the valleys environment, the most graphic symbol of the spirit of the community. Reclamation continues to take place, the pit-heads being replaced by green slopes, lakes, streams, trees and heritage parks. Some are fine efforts, but sadly the construction of many simply emphasizes their artificiality.

I returned to the lower Ebbw Valley to where Celynen South Colliery once stood. Summer undergrowth was slowly covering the concrete rubble, all that remained of the former colliery. Thistles, lilac bushes, birches and alders were springing up to herald a new era as nature healed the scars left by man. This 'wild reclamation' was the most beautiful of all – by comparison, man is an amateur. Here and there I came across remnants of the old railway sidings. The River Ebbw flows on as ever, but gone are the buildings and the winding towers. Gone also are the slag-heaps, the landscapes of hell, and the most hideous trappings of the coal industry. These monstrous mountains of black filth dominated the pit villages, and would probably have been left as a stark reminder of the days of coal, had it not been for Aberfan. Jean Thomas, in the last verse of her poem 'Miner' juxtaposes pit-head against slag-heap:

> But misty, greyed by distance,
> long outlines send their chill
> where the winding gear stands silent
> like a gallows on a hill.

This 'back to nature' policy of greening the valleys is, of course, one positive outcome of the decline of the pits, as industrial heritage trails and walks open up, enabling the visitor to explore and learn about the history of the coalfield at the same time. Opencast mining, which scars the landscape while being worked, is a cheaper alternative to deep mining, but provides far fewer jobs. In places it has a dreadful effect on local communities and

Site of Oakdale Colliery, Blackwood
The colliery was opened in 1908 by the Oakdale Navigation Company. Despite heavy investment it was closed down abruptly in 1990. The front entrance to Oakdale Colliery looked more like the approach to a manor-house than a coal-mine, with a lovely avenue of beeches. The site still bears the scars of past industry: twisted wire cables, lengths of rusting metal and huge wooden cable drums littered the huge site, but there remains no evidence of the colliery buildings. Nature has taken over, with Rosebay Willowherb and Ragwort much in evidence, and the oaks after which the village was named still forming a backdrop.

needs strict controls to reduce noise, dust levels and finally to ensure that proper restoration is carried out once the site is exhausted. New industries coming to the valleys can in no way take the place of the coal industry in terms of sheer employment capability.

As pits have closed, some miners have been shunted to other collieries, but now this option is no longer available. So the inevitable redundancy affects most miners in time. Many ex-miners mention how bitter and let-down they felt after working for many years in a pit, when told on a Wednesday that their mine was closing down on the Friday.

Miners, perhaps more so than any other workers, tend to regard

right

Penallta Colliery
Penallta Colliery, at Hengoed in Mid Glamorgan, was sunk around 1905 and extended in the 1960s. The pit-heads at Penallta were quite a challenge to fit into any really exciting composition, as I tried hard on both my visits to work out. My final visit was in October 1991, three weeks before the pit closed. After sketching some of the miners on a dull afternoon, when coal-dust seemed to hang in the air, we could hear them singing in the pit baths. Shortly afterwards those baths fell silent forever.

David Bellamy

the pit they work in as 'theirs'. While outsiders might find it difficult to see how anyone could get strong feelings about a hole in the ground, the pits do generate considerable emotive feelings among the miners. This emotion is a strong force behind the spirit of the valleys communities. The closing of the mines involved more than just finding alternative employment: it meant breaking up communities, forcing youngsters to leave for ever. How can the spirit of the people come to terms with this on such a massive scale? Three weeks before Penallta Colliery closed I was sketching on the surface when the morning shift emerged from the pit-head. They swelled out of the cage with the hungry aggression reminiscent of a Welsh rugby pack, as rough-hewn as the very rock they mined. Yet despite the fact that their pit was about to close, their humour came across with an irrepressible fire.

Portrait of Miner, Penallta Colliery

The trappings of a once-great industry from which sprang the evocative names of Deep Navigation, Six Bells, Taff Merthyr, Ferndale and Black Vein, have all but disappeared. Colliery hooters will never again echo across the valleys. Current generations can admire the reclaimed sites, sit and watch the streams tumble down hillsides that once shuddered with the shunting of a line of coal wagons, or imagine the clang of the cage or the shouts and laughter of the ghosts of miners. But future generations will not share these moments, these images, for they will never have witnessed the comradeship and spirit that was once a way of life for the valley people in their bitter struggle to eke a living out of the black gold.

CHAPTER FIVE

Capturing the Scenes

Painting mining scenes is absorbing and very exacting work, quite different from landscape painting – my usual subject area. At one time the South Wales valleys provided almost limitless opportunities for the artist who painted industrial scenery, but sadly there are now few opportunities to work directly from actual coal-mines. Apart from the sites mentioned in chapter six, artists can now only work from secondary sources such as old sketches and photographs. Even the valley towns and villages themselves are changing as modern buildings are erected and new roads create a nightmare for artist and pedestrian alike. If you study the terraced houses, you will see that many lovely old chimneys have disappeared, and these are often the best feature on a house as far

right

Miners' Cottages, Pontycymer

Pontycymer lies in the beautiful steep-sided Garw Valley, north of Bridgend. Close to this scene is the site of the old Ffaldau Colliery, which was sunk between 1876 and 1878. Ffaldau Colliery was one of the first in Wales to undergo major modernization, which was completed in 1949. It merged with Ocean Colliery in 1975 and was finally closed around 1978.

Blacksmith's Shop, Big Pit

In order to achieve this painting I needed two sketches: one of the smithy at Big Pit, and the other of a working blacksmith. The sketch of the blacksmith was carried out at the Welsh Folk Museum at St Fagans, where I managed to catch David Edwards in action. Apart from the manner in which the tools were gripped, the most important aspect of this latter sketch was the effect of the fire. Both the fire and the reflected light thrown up provided quite a challenge. David Edwards himself looked a little too modern for the era I wished to portray, so I changed the appearance of the blacksmith a little.

David Bellamy

as the artist is concerned. Huddled lines of tall smoking chimneys create that wonderful atmosphere of valley life.

The illustrations in this book fall into two categories: firstly the sketches done on the spot, and secondly the watercolour paintings carried out in the studio from the source material. At no time did I attempt to complete a finished watercolour on site, for several reasons: the subjects were mainly complicated ones involving a lot of time, which would have meant many visits to the same site; the environment was rarely conducive to delicate handling of watercolour paints; and, lastly, I have a preference for returning to my studio with the sketches and considering the work in depth before injecting a suitable atmosphere into the subject. In many instances these scenes also benefited from the addition or removal of certain objects, and this was more easily done at home.

Pencil is the most effective medium to use when sketching – a pencil and pad can be taken almost anywhere. Charcoal is also a superbly sensitive medium for capturing mood, really conducive to mining scenes, and it certainly worked well underground! These are both essentially drawing mediums, and really it is the drawing which is fundamental to achieving a competent painting of a coal-mine. I did do a small number of watercolour sketches, but actually this was not necessary, as I make colour notes on my pencil sketches where appropriate. While on site I sketched as many views of the pit-head gear and other important features as I could, being well aware even from the earliest visits that one day these mines would be lost for ever. I returned to many of the

Studio Sketch of Cefn Coed

This is a simple studio sketch drawn to determine the optimum position for all the major components within the composition. Notes around the drawing give some idea of my thinking as the planning progressed. Although I have mentioned snow on one side, in the end I decided against using it.

locations for further information and material, and, as always, found extra subjects that had been missed on a previous occasion.

To back up the sketches I took a number of photographs, which were especially useful where a lot of repetitive patterns on the metalwork were involved. They also helped to check angles and relationships, and of course those features where I had missed something out or managed to fudge in some way. My habit of quickly diverting to do a fleeting sketch of a miner who might sometimes appear briefly, was very effective in capturing figures, but did mean that I would sometimes forget what I had been doing originally and perhaps not complete a vital feature! So photographs were a considerable help, but needed great care in

Coming off Shift, Britannia Colliery

I came across Britannia Colliery quite by accident, while on a short-cut, and took the opportunity to get some detail within a whisker of it finally disappearing. The pit was sunk around 1912 near the village of Pengam, and the shafts were over 2,400 feet deep. It was closed in 1983.

The emphasis here is on the miners and I have tried to consider them as a group rather than as individuals. The background shed has been suggested rather than detailed so that it does not compete with the figures.

interpretation, as a wide-angle lens can exaggerate the size and angle of the subject, especially if it is close to the camera. Gaining a full understanding of the subject can only be done by sketching, for on coming across confusing features it is normally fairly easy to move closer to examine the problem, whereas with a photograph you would inevitably need to return to the site – if it is still there.

Many of the features could be sketched quite easily from outside the mine, and this usually had the advantage of allowing me to place the mine in its setting. This was particularly effective if the pit was hemmed in at the bottom of the valley with rows of houses close by, so typical of many Welsh pits. However, a closer view of the colliery buildings and equipment was essential in most cases, sometimes simply to find out what a heap of slag reflected in an oily puddle looked like! Ideally I made an appointment to visit the pit, but sometimes I would come upon one unexpectedly, and, if the light was right, I had to capture it then and there. In every case I found the miners and management extremely helpful and courteous. Many showed great patience in explaining how things worked, or the purpose of some of the more esoteric bits of equipment.

Sketching underground presents quite a different challenge. I had done a certain amount of underground sketching in caves before going down my first mine, so I was not entirely unaware of the potential problems. Apart from having to contend with the dirt and dust, the main difficulty is of course the lighting. Down in

Detail of Truck, Merthyr Vale

This is from part of the painting shown on page 80, and is highlighted here to illustrate how the further pit-head winding gear has been softened off to suggest distance. Even though it was a fine day with clear visibility, by using this technique the two pit-heads do not clash for attention. The bright yellow truck is strongly picked out, which also has the effect of pushing back the pit-head.

the coal-mines there was very little overhead lighting, and if there had been it would have detracted from the dramatic images conjured up by miners' lamps. My own headlamp gave a dull, flat lighting, hardly ideal for an exciting composition. The best and most atmospheric lighting came when three or four miners grouped together, when I attempted to sketch images caught in their lights. Much of this happened in a fleeting moment, often the juxtaposition of lamp and a second miner moving into the light, made more atmospheric by clouds of dust. Where miners were heavily engrossed in their work and steadily directing their lamps in one direction, this again brought excellent results. Some sketches were started, only to be abandoned as the subject disappeared completely.

The other main problem was the amount of time I could spend on each subject. While everything was simplified automatically by a lack of light, bits of interesting machinery really called out for much more time to be spent on the drawing. This required a decisive approach allied to a need to grasp the most important features of the subject, something which it is necessary to be attuned to before venturing off on an important sketching session. A kind of shorthand drawing system greatly enhances the chances of achieving a reasonably complete sketch, and after most of these trips I found myself filling in the gaps as soon afterwards as possible, based mainly on my shorthand hieroglyphics. Naturally, underground sketches done in such an environment became filthy, with coal-dust on everything. A number needed transcribing on to clean paper while the image remained fresh in my mind, otherwise the combination of dirt, and at times, confused drawing in the dark, could easily make the original sketch totally unintelligible.

Attention to detail is vital when out sketching, as this imbues the work with authenticity. For instance, if I came across a coal dram in an interesting position underground I would simply outline its shape, thereby ascertaining its position, relative size and perspective aspects, and perhaps concentrate on how the light is falling on one part of it, or the background detail. Other drams on the surface can provide models for sketching in more comfortable surroundings. To me it is essential to achieve a sense

overleaf

Markham Colliery

Markham Colliery, named after the company chairman Arthur Markham, was sunk in 1913, north of Blackwood in Gwent. In 1979 its underground workings were linked to those of Oakdale Colliery. Markham finally closed in 1985.

In this painting I have subdued the background pit-head so that it doesn't clash with the closer one. The rails have been faded out towards the foreground so that they are not too overwhelming.

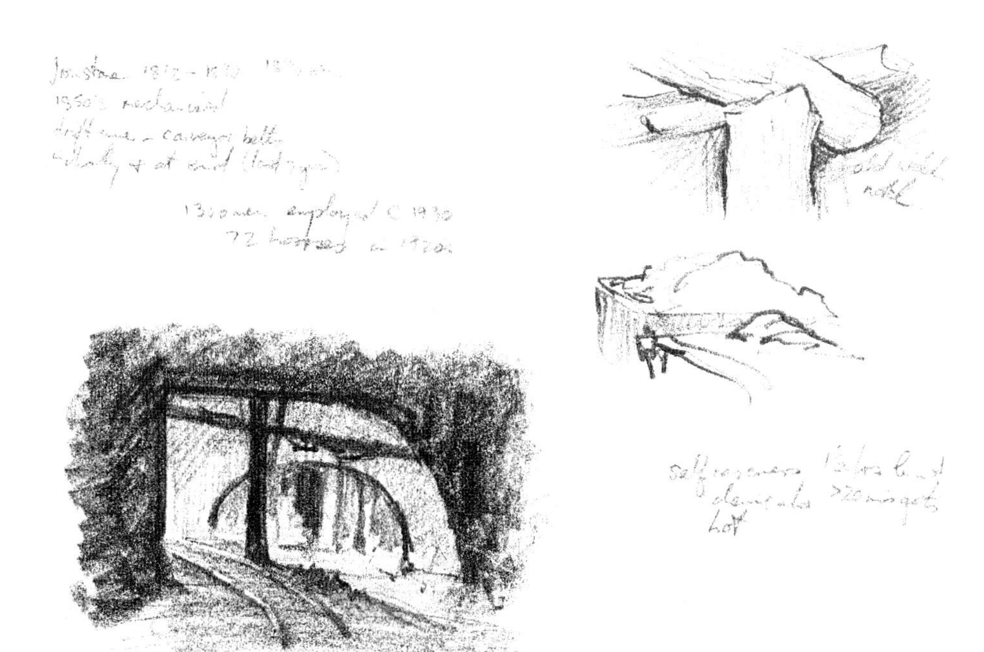

Underground Junction, Big Pit

of place in my work, so there is a strong need to observe aspects of the subject that are typical of that location.

Back in the studio I amass all the sketches, photographs and notes made on location, and then plan the final painting. With any complicated scene I find it well worth taking the trouble to draw simple studio or thumbnail sketches to give an idea as to how I want the final composition to appear. Sometimes it helps to carry out several of these little sketches to determine the optimum composition. The emphasis placed on one part of the scene in the sketch might be altered slightly for the painting to strengthen its impact, or maybe a figure or a coal dram added to provide some interest or life in an otherwise bare patch. This is why doing little studies of pieces of equipment and figures is so rewarding in the final analysis. At times all that is required is to move a feature slightly, but in a painting of a coal-mine this needs care, as an understanding of the relationship of the various parts is often vital.

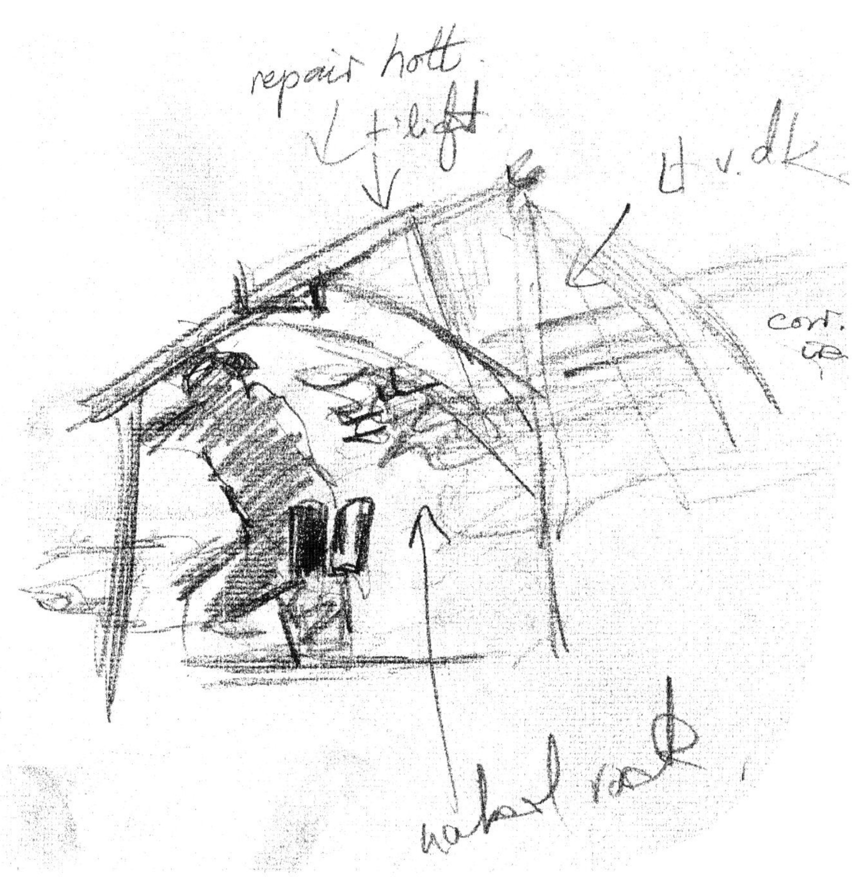

Repair Holt (original sketch)
This shows the rapid on-the-spot type of sketch sometimes necessary when time is limited. I use a sort of shorthand technique whereby only part of the stonework is rendered, for example. The sketch has been enhanced by coal-dust!

The paintings fall into two categories. Basically most of

them have been carried out as the subject appears, with perhaps a little modification, as already mentioned. The other category embraces those reconstructed scenes, or as in one or two cases, part-reconstructed. In a book of this type, being able to reconstruct scenes from the past in an authentic manner is an important feature requiring a lot of visual research. I shall describe the normal painting methods shortly. In the meantime let's look at some of the reconstruction techniques.

Reconstructing scenes from the past is a fascinating occupation, but fraught with all sorts of problems. These paintings took much longer, and necessitated a greater degree of effort than the ordinary ones painted from existing scenes. It became quite a challenge to dig out, detective-like, each part of the scene and build it up painstakingly like some protracted jigsaw puzzle. Each reconstructed scene was built up from a variety of sources. Most of the old pieces of equipment depicted in these scenes, whether anvils or ancient coal drams, were sketched at museums. Old photographs and records provided a clue as to which railway locomotives, for example, were employed in moving coal. Railway locomotives of the type working on coal duties were sought out at railway preservation centres, although I

Repair Holt (studio sketch)
Immediately on getting home after being down the mine I carried out a number of more finished studio sketches like this one. Here I have expanded my shorthand efforts and taken more care, adding in any features that could be remembered and drawn with confidence.

David Bel

did come across one old pannier tank locomotive quite by accident in the centre of Cardiff! It was necessary to obtain several angles on the locomotives, as even a slight alteration can present dreadful problems. Just one rivet out of place can cause a lot of steam in some quarters! Railway wagons in the livery of the old mining companies were found in the Welsh Industrial and Maritime Museum. Period clothes were 'draped on' to modern-day miners, and of course many locations have not changed at all over the last century, for example, small areas of buildings. Private mines also came in useful on occasion, for such things as the on-site pit ponies which are still used.

I visited many sites, some of which revealed virtually nothing of their heydays, and in some cases I did a considerable amount of research into mines which was not used eventually. Whenever I set out on a potential reconstruction I was only too aware that all the time and effort might well be in vain. Maps, site plans, books, photographs and various other scraps of information helped to piece the picture together, but often there was a vital feature missing. Nevertheless, occasionally something really exciting would occur to make it all worthwhile. A number of my earliest sketches turned out to be less than adequate, usually lacking in sufficient detail or not providing a complete picture, and so these often needed to be part-reconstructed in some way. A simple example of this was at Six Bells, where I wanted to include the rows of terraced houses creeping along the hillside above the mine. The original sketch did not concentrate on the houses, and

left

Big Pit, Blaenafon

Big Pit is now a mining museum. It is certainly a very 'paintable' place, with the wonderful old shanty-like tram circuit snaking its way along the contours to the left of the main buildings. The mine was sunk in 1860, and until it closed in 1980, it was the oldest working mine in South Wales.
The textures on the walls and heaps intrigued me and I have tried to accentuate these. As I approached the extremities of the paper the detail has been eased off so that nothing will pull the eye away from the focal point, which is the pit-head gear.

so I needed to return to Abertillery to draw in the houses – the easiest of all the problems encountered in this project.

The actual painting of reconstructed scenes involved a greater degree of planning than is normal. Before any preliminary drawing could be carried out, the various disparate elements of the picture had to be brought together in a realistic way. Even with all the material from one source this procedure was vital. The first stage usually involved linking diagrams and small sketches to work out the positions of all the various features within the overall picture. Gaps in the scene could be filled with figures, coal drams, or whatever, but it was essential that these were in scale and in keeping with the other elements. The vignette technique – losing the corners and softening the edges of a picture in the manner of Victorian photographs – worked well with reconstructed scenes. Not only did it put across a feeling of the past, but unnecessary or non-existent detail could be eliminated.

Watercolour is perhaps not the most obvious medium to use when painting industrial scenes. Having to work from light to dark in terms of tones, it presents more headaches than, for example, oil paints would, which allow the artist to overlay light tones over dark – a common need in mining scenes – where the light is often coming from several different sources. Complex industrial structures are normally easier to build up in oil paints. The challenge has been exciting, and involved some slightly different methods of working from normal landscape techniques. The newcomer to painting industrial scenery might benefit from

Miner Outside Lamp Room

Even in the 1990s, dress was not standard with the miners. They all had orange overalls available, but many seemed to prefer their old sweaters and shirts, which certainly was a welcome variation.

In order to make the figure stand out I painted in the background first, and when it was completely dry washed it over with a transparent watercolour wash. This had the effect of softening off the background without completely losing the detail. I then accentuated the tears and folds in the miner's sweatshirt, and the grime on his face.

using acrylic or gouache paints, at least initially, until some practice has been achieved. This is even more important when it is realized that many of these subjects are so complicated that they take far longer to accomplish than most landscapes, so the investment in time is much greater.

With normal watercolour techniques one paints with the lighter colours first, gradually building up to the darker ones. This is because watercolour is transparent and it is difficult to effectively paint a light colour onto a dark one and make it show up clearly. Without care it can resemble mud! Where, for example, there are light girders against a dark background, I had to paint on the lighter colour of the girders first, and, when this was dry, paint in the dark background shapes. This involved painting all the little negative shapes, i.e. the patterns between the actual girders.

Most of the paintings have been carried out on Saunders Waterford 140 lb Hot Pressed paper, although some have been done on rougher and tinted surfaces. The advantage of using the smooth Hot Pressed paper is that the strong detail is rendered more clearly, but the surface is less forgiving than a Not surface, which is a little rougher. The tinted surface used in the paintings of Taff Merthyr Colliery and Tirpentwys coal wagons gives a greater sense of unity and mood, but generally needs the introduction of white paint to create the highlights. Choice of paper is the most important aspect of watercolour painting and it pays to experiment with different surfaces.

Rendering industrial subjects in a reasonably realistic manner requires a high degree of accuracy. This is particularly important in the case of individual mines. Not only does the artist need to make worn metal look like worn metal, but miners who worked at a particular mine are likely to be highly critical of inaccuracies in the rendering of their pit. If every nut and bolt is included, however, the overall effect is too repetitive and overworked. To counter this a number of techniques were used. In places the detail in most paintings has been lost completely, or subdued to

Coming to Bank, Big Pit

Although much detail is in evidence, the scene has been considerably simplified, particularly in the area behind the chains linking the cage with the cable. I like to seek out little humorous touches like the little teddy bear on the notice board. I deliberately timed my visit so that the lighting would be just right.

avoid boring repetition. For example, rarely have miners' feet been drawn, or all the panes of glass in a window, or stones in a wall. When a few panes or stones are indicated, the eye of the viewer will automatically put in the rest, and, of course, if everything is stated there is no mystery about the work.

Clear, bright sunlight is not always the best weather to paint in – sometimes one can see too much! Where there are two lots of pit-head winding gear standing next to each other the detail on one becomes inextricably tangled up in that of the other as far as the artist can see when trying to unravel the scene. My answer has been to subdue or 'soften' the further one, as can be seen in the paintings of Markham Colliery and Merthyr Vale. This not only avoids the confusion, but pushes the further pit-head into the distance.

Another pitfall involved the mining museums. At Big Pit it has been noticeable over the years how much greener the surrounding area has become in the absence of industrial activity. The temptation to put in all that lovely grass has to be avoided, as to be really authentic it is essential to muck it up a bit! In a painting it is all too easy to put over a sanitized, clean appearance, which of course in a subject such as a coal-mine implies totally the wrong image. Coal-mines are generally littered with industrial detritus, and when I visited the Lewis Merthyr Colliery at the Rhondda Heritage Centre, I found the yards had been cleaned up to a high degree. So in the final painting I had to introduce a junkyard look from objects sketched at other mines. Working on

Paul Tucker, Cutterman

detailed studies of even small pieces of equipment was extremely beneficial, as these could be brought into a scene where perhaps extra foreground detail was required.

In order to convey something of the atmosphere of the pit I have deliberately reduced the number of colours used. Some of the paintings are virtually monochromes – a series of greys with the highlights left as white paper, and often just a hint of yellow or blue in the sky. Many compositions benefit from a splash of colour, though, especially around the main centre of interest. This was often provided by the orange overalls of the men, who, as well as lending a little colour, suggested a sense of scale.

Detail of Figures, Britannia Colliery
In this scene, shown in full on page 108, with so many figures, I felt it was important to show some of the miners actually relating to one another. Here that is achieved by making the second figure from the right turn round towards his colleagues. It is all too easy to consider each figure in isolation rather than as a group.

The miners themselves were very cooperative when asked to pose – some even asked to be sketched. 'A portrait for the kids', was the usual request, so at times I ended up doing two versions. Apart from the close-up portraits I did countless fleeting figures at various distances and at all attitudes, so that they could fit in to a number of paintings. One miner would often provide several studies. Moving groups of miners were not so easy to capture on paper. They had to be seen as a mass and in this case the way they related to each other was more important than individual details. The camera helped enormously here. Naturally, miners were sketched on one location and included in work on a totally different mine. One character is featured in three or four of the paintings. The best sketches were those where the men were busily engaged in some work or action. One of the most complicated sketching moments happened at Big Pit when no less than eleven coachloads of schoolchildren arrived and were brought through the point where I was working!

In many of the paintings, especially the more complicated ones, the background skies are less important. Often, however, the tall pit-head winding gear thrusts up into a sky with little else around it, thus needing quite a large area of sky in the work. In these paintings I have not only tried to include a more interesting sky than usual, but used cloud formations to balance the composition. Examples of this technique are where I have introduced strong clouds away from the pit-heads, or accentuated the pit-head with a light background and surrounded by more detailed cloud studies.

Painting the mining scenes has called for a tighter rein on my approach, but by emphasizing the skies and atmosphere the strong detail has to a degree been counter-balanced. This 'creative balancing' aspect of the work has proved to be the most demanding, but extremely enjoyable.

The aim of this chapter has been to give an insight into my methods of working, and hopefully encourage more artists to have a go at painting mining subjects. I hope it also inspires more people to take up painting.

CHAPTER SIX

FOLLOWING THE TRAIL

In this chapter those mining museums and other places of historical interest that are open to the public are listed, together with a few notes on each. While some of them are wholly devoted to the history of coal-mining, a number include mining as part of the local heritage, in which case it may only be represented in a small way. At some of the locations temporary exhibitions on certain aspects of mining are shown from time to time, so it is worth finding out if anything special is being featured before making a visit. Most of the museums publish informative brochures and booklets. Many of these sites are illustrated in this or the preceding chapters.

The list that follows is in alphabetical order, implying no particular order of importance

Afan Argoed Welsh Miners Museum

CYNONVILLE, PORT TALBOT, WEST GLAMORGAN

Tel: 0639 850564

The museum was created by miners and portrays the industry through the eyes of the miner. A traditional miner's cottage interior, photographs and memorabilia on coal-mining, the story of children working underground, and early mining equipment are among the many exhibits displayed in an interesting manner. Outdoor exhibits include a pit wheel, haulage engine and a coal tram. There are facilities for the disabled. Afan Argoed is situated in a beautiful setting, with a number of waymarked walks leaving the centre. It is located on the A4107, 6 miles north-east of Port Talbot.

Big Pit Mining Museum

BLAENAFON, GWENT

Tel: 0495 790311

See painting on page 116

Here you can descend the 294 foot shaft and be taken on an underground tour, complete with helmet, cap-lamp and self-rescuer, guided by an ex-miner. Apart from the tall pit-head gear and the winding engine-house, other fascinating buildings include the blacksmith's shop and the pit-head baths. There is a permanent exhibition illustrating the history of the South Wales Coalfield.

Future developments at Big Pit include the re-erection of a 160-year-old water-balance wheel with associated interpretation on the history of winding equipment; the acquisition of a 120-year-old Waddle fan with an associated interpretation on mine ventilation; and the extension of the modern mining display. Big Pit is proud that with well over one million underground visitors, to date they have not even had a single broken finger!

The museum is situated by the B4248 between Blaenafon and Brynmawr.

Cefn Coed Colliery Museum

BLAENANT COLLIERY, CRYNANT, NEATH, WEST GLAMORGAN

Tel: 0639 750556

See painting on page 128

The museum is on the site of the former Cefn Coed Colliery which was once the deepest anthracite coal-mine in the world. The main features include a massive steam winding engine which formerly raised and lowered the cages in the shaft, the boiler house, winding headgear, and a fascinating exhibition outlining the geology and mining history of the area. The mining gallery illustrates the changing methods of mining at Cefn Coed over the years. Don't miss the smaller exhibits outside, which include some ancient coal drams, a cage, and modern hydraulic roof supports. The museum is near Crynant, five miles north of Neath on the A4109.

Cefn Coed No. 2 Pit-head

Cefn Coed, at depths of over 2,500 feet, was once the deepest anthracite mine in the world. Coal was first raised there in 1930 after great problems in sinking the shafts. During the early years the colliery earned the nickname of 'The Slaughterhouse', for there were so many deaths. The mine finally closed in April 1968, and is now a colliery museum. The view here shows the No. 2 downcast shaft. There were two cages in each shaft and each cage could hold thirty men or two coal drams.

Dean Forest Railway

NORCHARD, LYDNEY, GLOUCESTERSHIRE

Tel: 0594 843423

Although the railway itself was originally built in 1809 as a horse-drawn tramway to haul the forest's mineral resources, the centre has nothing to do with the coal industry. I include it here because I sketched some of the locomotives that had been used on coal duties in the past.

Glyn Pits, Pontypool

JUST SOUTH OF THE A472 TOWARDS CRUMLIN, GRID REF. ST265999

See sketch on page 26

The site comprises three stone-built buildings, including an engine house containing a Cornish type beam pumping engine manufactured at the Neath Abbey Engineering Works in 1845. An easy half-mile walk (not sign-posted) leads to the site at the edge of a wood.

Hetty Shaft, Hopkinstown, Rhondda Valley

BESIDE THE A4225 SLIGHTLY NORTH-WEST OF PONTYPRIDD

See sketch on right

The pit-head and winding house still stand beside the main railway line. The foot-bridge over the railway provides an excellent viewpoint.

Hetty Shaft, Hopkinstown
In this close-up of Hetty shaft the aim was to bring out some of the detail on the metalwork.

Pontypridd Cultural Centre

LOCATED IN A CONVERTED CHAPEL BESIDE PONTYPRIDD BRIDGE

Tel: 0443 402077

The centre contains exhibits on local industrial history, temporary exhibitions and many other items of historical importance. The recorded voices telling stories of historical events are particularly interesting.

Rhondda Heritage Park

LEWIS MERTHYR, COED CAE ROAD, TREHAFOD, MID GLAMORGAN

Tel: 0443 682036

See painting on page 44

The main buildings of the old Lewis Merthyr Colliery have been turned into huge industrial theatres telling the story of the mining communities. The rich heritage of the valleys is brought to life in 'Black Gold – The Story of Coal', a very moving audio-visual presentation. Guides, many of whom are ex-miners, provide a guided tour, and as well as the two pit-heads with associated mining equipment, there is an exhibition showing reconstructions of a miner's cottage, a cage and underground tunnel among others. There is also an art gallery upstairs which has a changing programme of exhibitions. A themed play area for children has recently been added to the attractions. The Rhondda Heritage Park is situated a short distance off the A470.

South Wales Miners' Library

UNIVERSITY COLLEGE OF SWANSEA, HENDREFOELAN, SWANSEA, WEST GLAMORGAN

Tel: 0792 201231 extension 2003

The library houses books from the Miners Institute Libraries and a large collection of documents, posters and photographs, together with some of the trade union banners.

Valley Inheritance Museum

PARK BUILDINGS, PONTYPOOL, GWENT

Tel: 0495 752036

Housed in the Georgian stable block of Pontypool Park House, the exhibits tell the story of the Torfaen Valley, which includes a section on local coal-mining history. There is a regular changing programme of exhibitions. The museum is located in Pontypool.

Welsh Industrial and Maritime Museum

BUTE STREET, CARDIFF

Tel: 0222 481919

The museum illustrates the story of industrial and maritime growth in Wales during the last two centuries. A series of temporary exhibitions, some on coal-mining, are organized, so it is worth finding out what is on display before visiting. The permanent exhibition includes displays of industrial machinery and the development of transport. A number of old railway wagons in the livery of the coal companies prior to nationalization are featured. The museum is located in Cardiff's docklands, which grew in importance with the development of the coal industry.

Whistle Inn, Garn yr Erw

LOCATED JUST WEST OF THE B4248 BETWEEN BLAENAFON AND BRYNMAWR

See sketch below

Whistle Inn, Garn yr Erw
Here the inn is seen looking northwards up the track of the Pontypool and Blaenavon Steam Railway, with tank engine 'Nora' pushing a passenger train up the line. For safety reasons on the valley lines standard procedure was for locomotives to operate from the lower end of the train, to prevent any runaways. 'Nora' was originally used on coal duties at Big Pit.

A fascinating collection of over eighty antique miners lamps is on display at the inn, which stands within sight of Big Pit Mining Museum. The lamps range from an old candle-holder to the later types of safety lamp, and were donated to the inn by miners.

Other Sites of Interest

There are quite a number of industrial and heritage trails opening up in the valleys, often on former colliery sites. Some of them feature interpretive panels or leaflets, and up-to-date details can normally be obtained from the local tourist information centres.

Tower Colliery, Hirwaun
The viewpoint is on the mountainside, with the Ffyndaff opencast site beyond the colliery. As the underground workings emerge as a drift mine away to the right of the picture, there is no need for a second shaft for ventilation.

Glossary of Terms

BANK The top of the mine shaft where the cage stops.

BIAT Timber sleepers that secure the rails that steady the cage to the side of the shaft.

BLACKLEG A striking miner's term for a strike-breaker.

BRADISH CLOTH *see Brattice*

BRATTICE Rough cloth impregnated with tar, normally used to control the airflow.

BUTTY A friend or colleague. In England the term was used to refer to a middleman who sub-contracted colliers for the owners.

CAGE Lift used for carrying men, coal and materials up and down the shafts.

CHECK-WEIGHER A man who checked the weight of coal in each dram on behalf of the colliers, and was paid by them.

CHOKE-DAMP Carbonic gas.

COLLIER The miner who actually cuts the coal out, as opposed to other underground workers.

COMING TO BANK Arriving at the pit-head.

COMPANY UNIONISM Trade unions set up and controlled by the company, and opposed to taking strike action.

CURLING BOX A box used to carry coal between the face and the dram.

DOWNCAST SHAFT Air is sucked down this shaft.

DRAM Wheeled truck into which the coal is loaded for transportation underground.

DRIFT Sloping entrance to a mine.

FIRE-DAMP Methane gas.

FIREMAN Official who examines the mine for gas and carries out safety inspections.

GOB The area abandoned by the workings.

HAULIER A man leading the horses during transportation.

HEADING The main tunnel driven into the coal connecting with the main haulage roadway.

INBYE Going away from the shaft.

KIBBLE A large bucket used in the sinking of a shaft to carry men and supplies, and also to bring out waste.

LAGGING Timber walls used behind the main supports to prevent loose rock falling into the roadway.

LEVEL A drift mine driven along a coal vein.

LONGWALL A method of mining the coal with a single long coal-face.

MANDRIL Similar to a pick-axe.

OPENCAST Digging for coal near the surface by removing the topsoil and rock to expose the coal seams.

OUTBYE Going towards the shaft.

PILLAR AND STALL Method using separate 'stalls', each a few yards wide, for mining the coal, leaving behind 'pillars' of coal to support the roof.

PIT BOTTOM The area immediately around the bottom of the shaft.

SCREENS The place on the surface where coal was graded.

SPRAG Short lengths of timber pushed through the spokes of a dram to act as a brake, or to hold up low sections of roof.

TIPPLER A machine used to empty drams by turning them upside down.

TRAM As dram.

UNDERCUTTING Cutting a gap below the seam.

UPCAST SHAFT The shaft through which stale air is drawn up out of the mine.

Bibliography

Adeney, Martin, and Lloyd, John, *The Miners' Strike 1984–5*, Routledge and Kegan Paul, London, 1986.

Egan, David, *Coal Society – A History of the South Wales Mining Valleys 1840–1980*, Gomer Press, 1987.

Griffin, A.R., *The Collier*, Shire Publications Limited, Aylesbury, 1982.

Keen, Richard, *Coalface*, National Museum of Wales, Cardiff, 1991.

Orwell, George, *The Road to Wigan Pier*, Gollancz, 1937 (available in Penguin Books).

Thomas, Dr W. Gerwyn, *Welsh Coal Mines*, National Museum of Wales, Cardiff, 1979.

Williams, Roger, and Jones, David, *The Bitter Harvest*, Village Publishing, Pontypool, 1988.

Williams, Roger, and Jones, David, *The Cruel Inheritance*, Village Publishing, Pontypool, 1990.

Index

Illustrations are indicated by *italics*.

Abercarn 60
Abercwmboi 14
Abercynon Colliery *25*
Abercynon Miners' Institute *56*
Aberfan 79, 82, 99
Abertillery 20, *31*, 75, 82, 118
Ablett, Noah 88
Afan Argoed Welsh Miners Museum 126
Anthracite 29, 74
Arail Griffin Colliery 75

Barry Docks 28, 38
Bedlinog 21
Bell pits 27
Betws Colliery 95
Big Pit 20, 28, *29*, *47*, *61*, *104*, *111*, *116*, 117, *120*, 121,124, 127, 131, 132
Black Vein 102
Blackwood 100
Blaenafon 117, 127, 131
Blaengwrach Colliery 66
Blaenserchan Colliery 67, 95, *96–7*
Britannia Colliery *108*, *123*
British Coal 87, 90, 95
Brogden and Sons 24
Brynmawr 127, 131

Cambrian Colliery 82
Cambrian combine 38, 68, 71
Cardiff 12, 28, 38, 50, 117, 131
Carmarthenshire 29
Cefn Coed 28, 40, *41*, *107*, 127, *128*, 128
Celynen North Colliery 52, *53*
Celynen South Colliery *73*, 98
Children underground 31, 33
Coffin, Walter 27
Conservative government 84
Cory Brothers 24
Crynant 40, 127, 128
Cwm 68
Cynon Valley 27

Darby, Abraham 25
Davies, David 27, 28, 29
Davy lamp 42
Davy, Sir Humphrey 30, 42
Dean Forest Railway Centre 41, 50, 128
Deep Navigation Colliery 84, 102

Eastern Valley 57, 95
Ebbw, River 98, 99
Ebbw Vale Mining Company 60
Ebbw Vale Steel, Iron and Coal Company 68
Eckley, Archibald 15, 42, 51
Ely Colliery 68

Ferndale 60, 102
Ffaldau Colliery 104
Ffyndaff Opencast Site *83*, 132

Garn yr Erw 131
Garw Valley 16, 104
General Strike 72
Glamorgan 11, 29, 31, 68, 88, 100
Glamorgan Colliery 68
Glyn Pits *26*, 128
Gough, Mrs Annie 67, 75
Gray's Mine 20
Great Western Railway 38
Gwent 11, 14, 88, 95, 130

Hafodyrynys 15, 95
Hanbury Leigh, Capel 26
Hengoed 100
Hetty Shaft *18*, *48–9*, 50, 129, *129*
Hirwaun 19, 84, 132
Hopkinstown 18, 129
Horner, Arthur 88

Insole, George 27

Jones, James 30, 74
Jones, Lee 90, 91
Jones, Mordecai 12
Jones, Todd 40, 45, 50, 51, 67

Labour government 75, 79, 82
Lady Windsor Colliery 25
Lewis Merthyr Colliery *44*, 45, *87*, 121, 129
Lindsay, Lionel 68
Llanelli 38

Maerdy 30, 86, 87, 88
Maerdy Colliery 12, *13*, 16, 88, *89*
Marine Colliery 68, *69*
Markham Colliery *17*, 111, *112–13*, 121
Merthyr Consolidated Collieries 63
Merthyr Tydfil 26
Merthyr Vale Colliery 79, *80*, *109*, 121
Monmouthshire 29, 31, 55, 57, 60, 63
Mountain Ash 12, 72

National Coal Board 75, 79, 86, 87
National Union of Mineworkers 86
Neath 25, 26, 127
Newbridge 52
Newport 38
Nixon, John 27, 79
North's Navigation Collieries 24
North Wales 25, 31
Nottinghamshire 84, 86

Oakdale Colliery 100, 111
Oakdale Navigation Company 100
Ocean Coal Company 28
Ocean Colliery 104
Ogmore Vale 24
Opencast mining 27, 99
Orwell, George 35, 87

Pantglas Junior School 79
Pantygasseg 67
Pantygasseg Mine *33*, *82*
Partridge, Jones and Company 95
Pembrokeshire 12, 22
Penallta Colliery 100, *101*, 102
Penarth 38
Pengam 108
Penrhiwceiber Colliery *72*
Pneumoconiosis 67
Pochin Colliery *32*
Pontycymer 16, 104, *105*
Pontypool 22, 26, 42, 95, 128, 130
Pontypridd 70, 129
Pontypridd Cultural Centre 129
Port Talbot 38, 126
Powell, Thomas 27
Prince of Wales Colliery 60

Rhondda Heritage Centre 121, 129, 130
Rhondda Valley 15, 16, 27, 28, 29, 31, 52, 57, 60, 74, 87, 88, 129
Risca *39*
Royal Navy 38, 57

Senghenydd 63, *64*, 65
Sirhowy river 32
Six Bells Colliery 75, *76–7*, 82, 102, 117
South Wales Miners Federation 47
South Wales Miners' Library 130
Swansea 25, 26, 38, 130

Taff Merthyr *14*, *21*, 28, *36*, *66*, *78*, 90, *91*, *92*, *93*, 94, 95, 102, 119
Taff Vale Railway 28, 38
Tawe, River 26
Thomas, Jean 36, 46, 58, 99
Tirpentwys Colliery *15*, 33, 42, 95, 119
Tonypandy 68, 70
Torfaen Valley 130
Tower Colliery 19, *70*, *83*, 84, *85*, 98, *132*
Trades Union Congress 72, 73
Tredegar Iron and Coal Company 32
Tucker, Paul *122*

Universal Colliery 63, 65

Valley Inheritance Museum 130

Walker, Peter 20
Welsh Industrial and Maritime Museum 24, 32, 117, 131
Whistle Inn *131*, 131–2
Women Against Pit Closures 86
Wyndham Colliery *24*

Ynysybwl 25